endorsed by

Student S

*Higher*
# MATHEMATICS
## *for Edexcel GCSE*

## Tony Banks and David Alcorn

Causeway
Press

Pearson Education Limited
Edinburgh Gate
Harlow
Essex
CM20 2JE
England

ISBN-13: 978-1-4058-3500-8
ISBN-10: 1-4058-3500-1

**Endorsement**
This high quality material is endorsed by Edexcel and has been through a rigorous quality assurance
programme to ensure that it is a suitable companion to the specification for both learners and teachers.
This does not mean that its contents will be used verbatim when setting examinations, nor is it to be
read as being the official specification - a copy of which is available at   www.edexcel.org.uk

**Exam questions**
Past exam questions, provided by *London Examinations, a division of Edexcel*, are marked Edexcel.
The answers to all questions are entirely the responsibility of the authors/publisher and have neither
been provided nor approved by Edexcel.

Every effort has been made to locate the copyright owners of material used in this book.
Any omissions brought to the notice of the publisher are regretted and will be credited in
subsequent printings.

**Page design**
Billy Johnson

**Reader**
Barbara Alcorn

**Artwork**
David Alcorn

**Cover design**
Raven Design

Typesetting by Billy Johnson, San Francisco, California, USA

Printed and bound by Scotprint, Haddington, Scotland

# preface

This book provides detailed revision notes, worked examples and examination questions to support students in their preparation for the new two-tier GCSE Mathematics examinations for the Edexcel Specifications – Higher Tier.

The book has been designed so that it can be used in conjunction with the companion book *Higher Mathematics for Edexcel GCSE* or as a stand-alone revision book for self study and provides full coverage of the new Edexcel Specifications for the Higher Tier of entry.

In preparing the text, full account has been made of the requirements for students to be able to use and apply mathematics in written examination papers and be able to solve problems in mathematics both with and without a calculator.

The detailed revision notes, worked examples and examination questions have been organised into 40 self-contained sections which meet the requirements of the National Curriculum and provide efficient coverage of the specifications.

| | |
|---|---|
| Sections 1 - 9 | Number |
| Sections 10 - 22 | Algebra |
| Sections 23 - 34 | Shape, Space and Measures |
| Sections 35 - 40 | Handling Data |

At the end of the sections on Number, Algebra, Shape, Space and Measures and Handling Data, section reviews are provided to give further opportunities to consolidate skills.

At the end of the book there is a final examination questions section with a further compilation of exam and exam-style questions, organised for non-calculator and calculator practice, in preparation for the exams.

Also available *With Answers: (ISBN: 1-405835-01-X)*
The book has been designed so that it can be used in conjunction with the companion book
*Higher Mathematics for Edexcel GCSE (ISBN: 1-405831-44-8)*

# contents

## Number                                      Sections 1 - 9

## Algebra                                      Sections 10 - 22

# Shape, Space and Measures

**Section Review - Shape, Space and Measures**

# Handling Data

**Section Review - Handling Data**

**Exam Practice**

# Whole Numbers

## What you need to know

- You should be able to read and write numbers expressed in figures and words.
- Be able to recognise the place value of each digit in a number.

  **Eg 1** In the number 5384 the digit 8 is worth 80, but in the number 4853 the digit 8 is worth 800.

- Know the Multiplication Tables up to $10 \times 10$.
- Use non-calculator methods for addition, subtraction, multiplication and division.
- Know the order of operations in a calculation.

| **First** | Brackets and Division line |
|---|---|
| **Second** | Divide and Multiply |
| **Third** | Addition and Subtraction |

**Eg 2** $4 + 2 \times 6 = 4 + 12 = 16$

**Eg 3** $9 \times (7 - 2) + 3 = 9 \times 5 + 3 = 45 + 3 = 48$

- You should be able to add, subtract, multiply and divide with negative numbers.
- Be able to use these rules with negative numbers.

| **When adding or subtracting:** |
|---|
| $+ \; +$ can be replaced by $+$ |
| $- \; -$ can be replaced by $+$ |
| $+ \; -$ can be replaced by $-$ |
| $- \; +$ can be replaced by $-$ |

| **When multiplying:** |
|---|
| $+ \times + = +$ |
| $- \times - = +$ |
| $+ \times - = -$ |
| $- \times + = -$ |

| **When dividing:** |
|---|
| $+ \div + = +$ |
| $- \div - = +$ |
| $+ \div - = -$ |
| $- \div + = -$ |

**Eg 4** Work out.
(a) $(-5) - (-8) = -5 + 8 = 3$

(b) $(-2) \times (-3) = 6$

(c) $\dfrac{(-8) \times (+2) + (-4)}{(-5) \times (-1)} = \dfrac{-16 - 4}{5} = \dfrac{-20}{5} = -4$

## Exercise 1
Do not use a calculator for this exercise.

**1** (a) Write one million five thousand and ten in figures.
(b) Given that $235 \times 640 = 150\,400$, work out $1\,504\,000 \div 64$.

**2** Work out. (a) $7096 + 2974$ (b) $8042 - 1357$ (c) $731 \times 137$ (d) $2002 \div 13$

**3** (a) Using each of the digits 9, 2, 3 and 6 write down
(i) the largest odd number, (ii) the smallest even number.
(b) What is the answer when the smallest even number is subtracted from the largest odd number?

**4** Last year Mr Alderton had the following household bills.

| Gas | £364 | Electricity | £158 | Telephone | £187 |
|---|---|---|---|---|---|
| Water | £244 | Insurance | £236 | Council Tax | £983 |

He paid the bills by 12 equal monthly payments. How much was each monthly payment?

**5** Colin packs shirts in a factory. He packs 85 shirts a day.
Last year he packed shirts for 218 days. How many shirts did he pack last year?

**6** Work out $453 \times 73$.

Edexcel

**7** Naomi has collected £357 from her friends for concert tickets. The tickets cost £17 each. How many people have paid for tickets?

**8** Work out.
(a) $12 - 6 + 2$  (b) $12 \div 6 \times 2$  (c) $(27 + 8) \times 3$  (d) $\dfrac{9 - 4 + 3 \times 5}{2 \times 3 + 4}$

**9** Tom breeds hamsters for pet shops. The number of hamsters trebles each year. Tom has 20 hamsters at the end of Year 1.
(a) How many hamsters would Tom have at the end of 5 years?
(b) A hamster cage can hold no more than 14 hamsters.
Work out the minimum number of cages needed for 900 hamsters.

Edexcel

**10** Simon is 8 kg heavier than Matt. Their weights add up to 132 kg.
How heavy is Simon?

**11** A roll of wire is 500 cm long. From the roll, Debra cuts 3 pieces which each measure 75 cm and 4 pieces which each measure 40 cm. How much wire is left on the roll?

**12** Car Hire Co. have the following cars available to rent.

| Model | Corsa | Astra | Zafira |
|---|---|---|---|
| Number of cars | 10 | 12 | 6 |
| Weekly rental | £210 | £255 | £289 |

Work out the total weekly rental when all the cars are hired.

**13** Calculate.  (a) $\dfrac{10 \times 20 \times 30 \times 40 \times 50}{1 + 2 + 3 + 4 + 5}$  (b) $\dfrac{356 - 200 \div 25}{24}$

**14** This rule can be used to estimate the temperature in °F for temperatures given in °C.

> Multiply the temperature in °C by 2 and add 30.

Use this rule to estimate $-17$°C in °F.

**15** Work out.
(a) $(-9) - (-5) + (-3)$  (b) $\dfrac{(-7) \times (-3) - (-6)}{(-9)}$  (c) $\dfrac{(-3) \times (-5) - (-7) \times (+3)}{(-4) + (-2)}$

**16** A test has 12 questions.

> A correct answer scores $+3$ marks.
> An incorrect answer scores $-1$ mark.

Pippa attempts every question and scores 8 marks.
How many correct answers did she get?

**17** The number of bacteria in a certain colony doubles every day.
At the start of an experiment there are 96 bacteria.
How many bacteria will there be 10 days later?

**18** The prizes paid out in last Saturday's Lottery are shown in the table.

| Number of winners | Value of each prize |
|---|---|
| 1 | £6 469 676 |
| 27 | £73 728 |
| 708 | £1 757 |
| 41 422 | £66 |
| 812 558 | £10 |

How much was paid out in prizes in last Saturday's Lottery?

# Decimals and Fractions

## What you need to know

- You should be able to use non-calculator methods for addition, subtraction, multiplication and division of decimals.

  **Eg 1** Work out.

  (a) $5.1 \times 0.43$

$$\begin{array}{r} 5.1 \quad (1\,\text{d.p.}) \\ \times \ 0.43 \quad (2\,\text{d.p.}) \\ \hline 1\,5\,3 \leftarrow 51 \times 3 \\ + 2\,0\,4\,0 \leftarrow 51 \times 40 \\ \hline 2.1\,9\,3 \quad (3\,\text{d.p.}) \end{array}$$

  (b) $1.64 \div 0.2$

  $$\frac{1.64}{0.2} = \frac{16.4}{2} = 8.2$$

  > When a number is **multiplied** by a number between 0 and 1 the result will be **smaller** than the original number.
  > When a number is **divided** by a number between 0 and 1 the result will be **larger** than the original number.

- Be able to use decimals to solve problems involving money and other measures.

- The top number of a fraction is called the **numerator**, the bottom number is called the **denominator**.

- Fractions which are equal are called **equivalent fractions**. For example, $\frac{8}{20} = \frac{4}{10} = \frac{2}{5}$

  **Eg 2** Write $\frac{20}{28}$ as a fraction in its simplest form.

  $$\frac{20}{28} = \frac{20 \div 4}{28 \div 4} = \frac{5}{7}$$

  > Divide the numerator and denominator by the largest number that divides into both.

- $2\frac{1}{2}$ is an example of a **mixed number**. It is a mixture of whole numbers and fractions.

- $\frac{5}{2}$ is an **improper** (or 'top heavy') fraction.

- Fractions must have the **same denominator** before **adding** or **subtracting**.

  **Eg 3** Work out.

  (a) $\frac{3}{4} + \frac{2}{3} = \frac{9}{12} + \frac{8}{12} = \frac{17}{12} = 1\frac{5}{12}$

  (b) $\frac{4}{5} - \frac{1}{2} = \frac{8}{10} - \frac{5}{10} = \frac{3}{10}$

  > Add (or subtract) the numerators only. When the answer is an improper fraction change it into a mixed number.

- Mixed numbers must be changed to **improper fractions** before **multiplying** or **dividing**.

  **Eg 4** Work out.

  (a) $1\frac{1}{4} \times 2\frac{1}{5} = \frac{\overset{1}{\cancel{5}}}{4} \times \frac{11}{\underset{1}{\cancel{5}}} = \frac{11}{4} = 2\frac{3}{4}$

  > The working can be simplified by cancelling.

  (b) $1\frac{1}{3} \div 1\frac{3}{5} = \frac{4}{3} \div \frac{8}{5} = \frac{\overset{1}{\cancel{4}}}{3} \times \frac{5}{\underset{2}{\cancel{8}}} = \frac{5}{6}$

  > Dividing by $\frac{8}{5}$ is the same as multiplying by $\frac{5}{8}$.

- All fractions can be written as decimals.

  > To change a fraction to a decimal divide the **numerator** by the **denominator**.

  **Eg 5** Change $\frac{4}{5}$ to a decimal.

  $$\frac{4}{5} = 4 \div 5 = 0.8$$

- Some decimals have **recurring digits**. These are shown by:

  a single dot above a single recurring digit,

  **Eg 6** $\frac{2}{3} = 0.6666\ldots = 0.\dot{6}$

  a dot above the first and last digit of a set of recurring digits.

  **Eg 7** $\frac{5}{11} = 0.454545\ldots = 0.\dot{4}\dot{5}$

**1** (a) Lucy works out $0.2 \times 0.4$. She gets the answer 0.8.
Explain why her answer must be wrong.
(b) Work out. (i) $0.3 \times 0.4$   (ii) $0.3 \times 0.2$

**2** Work out. (a) $5 - 2.36$   (b) $4.8 \times 2.5$   (c) $0.294 \div 12$   (d) $\dfrac{54.4 \div 0.4}{0.2 \times 0.5}$

**3** Two pieces of wood of length 0.75 m and 2.68 m are sawn from a plank 5 m long.
What length of wood is left?

**4** Joseph did the following calculation: $28 \div 8.5 = 3.2$
(a) Write down the multiplication which Joseph could do to **check** his answer.
(b) Was Joseph's answer correct? Show your working.                    Edexcel

**5** Tim paid £5.44 for 17 pencils. Each pencil costs the same. Work out the cost of each pencil.
                                                                        Edexcel

**6**    $5 \times m$ **gives an answer** *less than 5.*    $5 \div m$ **gives an answer** *more than 5.*
Give two possible values for $m$ which satisfy **both** conditions.

**7** Ann wins £160. She gives $\frac{1}{4}$ of £160 to Pat, $\frac{3}{8}$ of £160 to John and £28 to Peter.
What fraction of the £160 does Ann keep? Give your fraction in its simplest form.   Edexcel

**8** (a) Write down a fraction that lies halfway between $\frac{1}{3}$ and $\frac{1}{2}$.
(b) An examination is marked out of 48. Ashley scored 32 marks.
What fraction of the total did he score? Give your answer in its simplest form.

**9** George pays £1.82 for $\frac{1}{5}$ kg of toffees at £4.20 per kilogram and $\frac{1}{4}$ kg of jellies.
How much per kilogram are jellies?

**10** Work out. (a) $\frac{1}{4} \times \frac{2}{3}$   (b) $2\frac{3}{8} - 1\frac{1}{4}$                    Edexcel

**11** (a) Change $\frac{1}{6}$ to a decimal. Give the answer correct to 3 d.p.
(b) Write these numbers in order of size, starting with the largest.

    | 1.067 | 1.7 | 1.66 | $1\frac{1}{6}$ | 1.67 |

(c) Change 0.65 to a fraction in its simplest form.

**12** Work out. (a) $2\frac{2}{3} + 3\frac{3}{4}$   (b) $\frac{3}{4} \times 1\frac{1}{5}$   (c) $4\frac{1}{2} \div \frac{3}{8}$

**13** Which of the following fractions is nearest to $\frac{3}{4}$?   | $\frac{7}{10}$ | $\frac{2}{3}$ | $\frac{7}{8}$ | $\frac{9}{11}$ |
Show how you decide.

**14** Work out. $3\frac{3}{4} \times 2\frac{2}{3}$                    Edexcel

**15** Income tax and national insurance take $\frac{1}{5}$ of Phillip's pay.
He gives $\frac{2}{5}$ of what he has left to his parents for housekeeping.
What fraction of his pay does Phillip have left for himself?

**16** Three-fifths of the people at a party are boys.
Three-quarters of the boys are wearing fancy dress.
What fraction of the people at the party are boys wearing fancy dress?

**17** In a sale the price of a microwave is reduced by $\frac{1}{5}$. The sale price is £96.
What was the price of the microwave before the sale?

**18** Work out. $\dfrac{12.9 \times 7.3}{3.9 + 1.4}$. Write down your full calculator display.

**19** Use your calculator to work out the exact value of $\dfrac{14.82 \times (17.4 - 9.25)}{(54.3 + 23.7) \times 3.8}$.
                                                                        Edexcel

# Approximation and Estimation

## What you need to know

- How to **round** to the nearest 10, 100, 1000.

- In real-life problems a rounding must be used which gives a sensible answer.

- How to approximate using **decimal places**.

  Write the number using one more decimal place than asked for.
  Look at the last decimal place and
  - if the figure is 5 or more round up,
  - if the figure is less than 5 round down.

  **Eg 1**   Write the number 3.649 to
  (a)   2 decimal places,
  (b)   1 decimal place.

  (a)   3.65,
  (b)   3.6.

- How to approximate using **significant figures**.

  Start from the most significant figure and count the required number of figures.
  Look at the next figure to the right of this and
  - if the figure is 5 or more round up,
  - if the figure is less than 5 round down.
  Add noughts, as necessary, to preserve the place value.

  **Eg 2**   Write each of these numbers correct to 2 significant figures.
  (a)   365
  (b)   0.0423

  (a)   370
  (b)   0.042

- You should be able to choose a suitable degree of accuracy.

  The result of a calculation involving measurement should not be given to a greater degree of accuracy than the measurements used in the calculation.

- Be able to use approximations to estimate that the actual answer to a calculation is of the right order of magnitude.

  Estimation is done by approximating every number in the calculation to one significant figure.
  The calculation is then done using the approximated values.

  **Eg 3**   Use approximations to estimate $\dfrac{5.1 \times 57.2}{9.8}$.

  $$\frac{5.1 \times 57.2}{9.8} = \frac{5 \times 60}{10} = 30$$

- Be able to use a calculator to check answers to calculations.

- Be able to recognise limitations on the accuracy of data and measurements.

  **Eg 4**   Jamie said, "I have 60 friends at my party." This figure is correct to the nearest 10. What is the smallest and largest possible number of friends Jamie had at his party?

  The smallest whole number that rounds to 60 is 55.
  The largest whole number that rounds to 60 is 64.
  So, smallest is 55 friends and largest is 64 friends.

  **Eg 5**   A man weighs 57 kg, correct to the nearest kilogram.
  What is the minimum weight of the man?
  Minimum weight = 57 kg − 0.5 kg = 56.5 kg.

  **Eg 6**   Calculate the upper bound of $\dfrac{a}{b}$ when:

  $a = 7.6$, correct to 2 sig. figs.,   and   $b = 50$, correct to 2 sig. figs.

  Upper bound of $\dfrac{a}{b} = \dfrac{\text{upper bound of } a}{\text{lower bound of } b} = \dfrac{7.6 + 0.05}{50 - 0.5} = \dfrac{7.65}{49.5} = 0.154545\ldots$

Do not use a calculator for questions 1 to 10.

**1** Write the result shown on the calculator display
(a) to the nearest ten,
(b) correct to one decimal place,
(c) correct to one significant figure.

**2** A newspaper's headline states: "20 000 people attend concert".
The number in the newspaper is given to the nearest thousand.
What is the smallest possible attendance?

**3** On Saturday a dairy sold 2975 litres of milk at 42 pence per litre.
By rounding each number to one significant figure, estimate the amount of money received from the sale of milk, giving your answer in pounds.

**4** (a) To estimate 97 × 49, Charlie uses the approximations 100 × 50.
Explain why his estimate will be larger than the actual answer.
(b) To estimate 1067 ÷ 48, Patsy uses the approximations 1000 ÷ 50.
Will her estimate be larger or smaller than the actual answer?
Give a reason for your answer.

**5** A concert hall has 22 rows of seats. Each row has 69 seats.
(a) Work out an approximate answer to the total number of seats in the concert hall.

Every person attending a concert pays £9.75 on entry. Every seat in the concert hall is filled.
(b) Work out the approximate amount of money taken at the concert hall.
*Edexcel*

**6** A car park has spaces for 640 cars, correct to the nearest ten.
What is the greatest possible number of spaces in the car park?

**7** In 2005, Mr Symms drove 8873 kilometres.
His car does 11 kilometres per litre. Petrol costs 89.9 pence per litre.
(a) By rounding each number to one significant figure, estimate the amount he spent on petrol.
(b) Without any further calculation, explain why this estimate will be larger than the actual amount.

**8** Explain how you can **estimate** the value of the following by approximating the three numbers and give your approximate answer. $\dfrac{0.251 \times 81.376}{5.096}$
*Edexcel*

**9** The string on a kite is 50 m in length, correct to the nearest metre.
What is the minimum length of the string?

**10** John made the statement:
**"If you are given a number written correct to 2 decimal places it is more accurate than when written correct to 2 significant figures."**
John chose 6.60 and 6.6 as examples.
(a) Explain clearly how John could use these numbers to justify his statement.
(b) Is John's statement always true? Justify your answer.
*Edexcel*

**11** (a) Calculate $\dfrac{88.3 \times 4.24}{72.5 - 9.87}$.
(b) By using approximations show that your answer to (a) is about right.
You **must** show all your working.
*Edexcel*

**12** A school orders 20 copies of a book. Each book weighs 0.46 kg, correct to 2 decimal places.
Calculate the lower bound and the upper bound of the total weight of the books.

**13** $p$ and $q$ are dimensions.
To an accuracy of two significant figures, $p = 25$ cm and $q = 12$ cm.
Calculate (a) the upper bound of $p - q$, (b) the lower bound of $\dfrac{p}{q}$.

## What you need to know

- 10% is read as '10 percent'. 'Per cent' means out of 100. 10% means 10 out of 100.
- A percentage can be written as a fraction, 10% can be written as $\frac{10}{100}$.
- To change a decimal or a fraction to a percentage: **multiply by 100**.
- To change a percentage to a fraction or a decimal: **divide by 100**.
- How to express one quantity as a percentage of another.

  **Eg 1** Write 30p as a percentage of £2.

  $\frac{30}{200} \times 100 = 30 \times 100 \div 200 = 15\%$

  > Write the numbers as a fraction, using the same units.
  > Change the fraction to a percentage.

- You should be able to use percentages to solve a variety of problems.
- Be able to find a percentage of a quantity.

  **Eg 2** Find 20% of £64.

  £64 ÷ 100 = £0.64
  £0.64 × 20 = £12.80

  > 1. Divide by 100 to find 1%.
  > 2. Multiply by the percentage to be found.

- Be able to find a percentage increase (or decrease).

  $$\text{Percentage increase} = \frac{\text{actual increase}}{\text{initial value}} \times 100\%$$

  $$\text{Percentage decrease} = \frac{\text{actual decrease}}{\text{initial value}} \times 100\%$$

  **Eg 3** Find the percentage loss on a micro-scooter bought for £25 and sold for £18.

  Percentage loss $= \frac{7}{25} \times 100 = 28\%$

- Be able to solve reverse percentage problems.

  **Eg 4** Find the original price of a car which is sold at a loss of 20% for £1200.

  80% of original price = £1200
  1% of original price = £1200 ÷ 80 = £15
  Original price = £15 × 100 = £1500

  > First find 1% of the original value by dividing the selling price by (100 − % loss), then multiply by 100.

- **Hourly pay** is paid at a **basic rate** for a fixed number of hours.
  **Overtime pay** is usually paid at a higher rate such as time and a half, which means each hour's work is worth 1.5 times the basic rate.
- Everyone is allowed to earn some money which is not taxed. This is called a **tax allowance**.
- Tax is only paid on income earned in excess of the tax allowance. This is called **taxable income**.

  **Eg 5** Tom earns £6080 per year.
  His tax allowance is £4895 per year and he pays tax at 10p in the £ on his taxable income.
  Find how much income tax Tom pays per year.

  Taxable income = £6080 − £4895 = £1185
  Income tax payable = £1185 × 0.10 = £118.50

  > First find the taxable income, then multiply taxable income by rate in £.

- **Value added tax**, or **VAT**, is a tax on some goods and services and is added to the bill.
- When considering a **best buy**, compare quantities by using the same units.
  For example, find which product gives more grams per penny.

- Money invested in a savings account at a bank or building society earns **interest**.
- With **Simple Interest**, the interest is paid out each year and not added to your account.

$$\text{Simple Interest} = \dfrac{\text{Amount}}{\text{invested}} \times \dfrac{\text{Time in}}{\text{years}} \times \dfrac{\text{Rate of interest}}{\text{per year}}$$

**Eg 6**  Find the Simple Interest paid on £600 invested for 6 months at 8% per year.

Simple Interest $= 600 \times \frac{6}{12} \times \frac{8}{100} = 600 \times 0.5 \times 0.08 = £24$

- With **Compound Interest**, the interest earned each year is added to your account and also earns interest the following year.

**Eg 7**  Find the **Compound Interest** paid on £600 invested for 2 years at 6% per year.

| **1st year** | | **2nd year** | |
|---|---|---|---|
| Investment | = £600 | Investment | = £636 |
| Interest: £600 × 0.06 | = £  36 | Interest: £636 × 0.06 | = £  38.16 |
| Value after one year | = £636 | Value after two years | = £674.16 |

Compound Interest = Final value − Original value = £674.16 − £600 = £74.16

*This could be calculated as:*  $600 \times (1.06)^2 - 600 = £74.16$

## Exercise 4

Do not use a calculator for questions 1 to 5.

**1**  What is 40 as a percentage of 500?

**2**  A test is marked out of 80. Colin scored 35% of the marks.
How many marks did Colin score?

**3**  A jacket normally costs £48. The price is reduced by 15% in a sale.
What is the price of the jacket in the sale?

**4**  Angela is paid £7.40 per hour for a basic 35-hour week. Overtime is paid at time and a half.
Last week Angela was paid £303.40.
How many hours did she work last week?

**5**  Mrs Tilsed wishes to buy a car priced at £2400.

> **Two options are available.**
> **Option 1** – A deposit of 20% of £2400 and 24 monthly payments of £95.
> **Option 2** – For a single payment the dealer offers a discount of 5% on £2400.

How much more does it cost to buy the car if option 1 is chosen rather than option 2?

**6**  Asif sells computers.
Each week Asif is paid £150 plus £20.50 for each computer he sells that week.
Last week Asif was paid £888.
(a)  Work out how many computers Asif sold last week.

Jane is going to buy a computer for £480 + $17\frac{1}{2}$% VAT.

(b)  Work out the total price, including VAT, that Jane will pay for the computer.  Edexcel

**7**  A pogo stick is bought for £12.50 and sold for £8.
What is the percentage loss?

**8**  Toffee is sold in bars of two sizes.
A large bar weighs 450 g and costs £1.69. A small bar weighs 275 g and costs 99p.
Which size of bar is better value for money? You must show all your working.

**9** A farmer has 200 sheep. 90% of the sheep have lambs.
Of the sheep which have lambs 45% have two lambs.
How many of the sheep have two lambs?

**10** Lily invests £1000 at 4.25% per annum simple interest.
She withdraws her money after 6 months.
How much interest did she get?

**11** Last year Leroy had a tax allowance of £4895 and paid £3520 in tax.
How much did Leroy earn last year if he paid tax at the rate of 10p in the £ on the first £2090
of his taxable income and 22p in the £ on all his remaining income?

**12** Shreena put £484 in a new savings account.
At the end of every year, interest of 4.3% was added to the amount in her savings account at
the start of that year.
Calculate the total amount in Shreena's savings account at the end of 2 years.          Edexcel

**13**

**1st STOP Car Insurance**

**Typical insurance:**
Vauxhall Corsa - £650 per year
No Claims Discount Available

(a) Vanessa has a Vauxhall Corsa. She is given a no claims discount.
After taking off her no claims discount she has to pay £390 to insure her car.
Calculate her no claims discount as a percentage of £650.

(b) Cedric has a BMW car. He is given a 65% no claims discount.
After the discount he has to pay £336 to insure his car.
Calculate the price of the insurance before the discount.

**14** A clothes shop has a sale.
All the original prices are reduced by 24% to give the sale price.
The sale price of a jacket is £36.86.
Work out the original price of the jacket.          Edexcel

**15** This report appeared in a motoring magazine.

In the first year of ownership a new car loses 20% of its value
and in the second year it loses 15% of its one-year old value.

If this report is true, what is the percentage loss in the value of a new car in its first 2 years?

**16** Questionnaires were sent to a number of people. 72 people replied.
This was only 18% of all the people that had been sent questionnaires.
How many people had been sent questionnaires?

**17** The price of a new television is £423. This price includes Value Added Tax at $17\frac{1}{2}$%.
(a) Work out the cost of the television **before** VAT was added.

By the end of each year, the value of a television has fallen by 12% of its value at the start of
that year.
The value of a television was £423 at the start of the first year.
(b) Work out the value of the television at the end of the **third** year.
Give your answer to the nearest penny.          Edexcel

**18** (a) Mike invests £3000 at 5% per annum compound interest.
What is the value of his investment after 3 years?
(b) Jayne invests her money at 6% per annum compound interest.
What is the percentage increase in the value of her investment after 3 years?

# Working with Number

**What you need to know**

- **Multiples** of a number are found by multiplying the number by   1,   2,   3,   4,   …

  **Eg 1**   The multiples of 8 are   $1 \times 8 = $ **8**,   $2 \times 8 = $ **16**,   $3 \times 8 = $ **24**,   $4 \times 8 = $ **32**,   …

- **Factors** of a number are found by listing all the products that give the number.

  **Eg 2**   $1 \times 6 = 6$   and   $2 \times 3 = 6$.   So, the factors of 6 are:   1,   2,   3   and   6.

- The **common factors** of two numbers are the numbers which are factors of **both**.

- A **prime number** is a number with only two factors, 1 and the number itself.
  The first few prime numbers are:   2,   3,   5,   7,   11,   13,   17,   19,   …
  The number 1 is not a prime number because it has only one factor.

- The **prime factors** of a number are those factors of the number which are prime numbers.

  **Eg 3**   The factors of 18 are:   1,   2,   3,   6,   9   and   18.
  The prime factors of 18 are:   2   and   3.

- The **Least Common Multiple** of two numbers is the smallest number that is a multiple of both.

  **Eg 4**   The Least Common Multiple of 4 and 5 is 20.

- The **Highest Common Factor** of two numbers is the largest number that is a factor of both.

  **Eg 5**   The Highest Common Factor of 8 and 12 is 4.

- An expression such as   $3 \times 3 \times 3 \times 3 \times 3$   can be written in a shorthand way as $3^5$.
  This is read as '3 to the power of 5'.
  The number 3 is the **base** of the expression. 5 is the **power**.

- Powers can be used to help write any number as the **product of its prime factors**.

  **Eg 6**   $72 = 2 \times 2 \times 2 \times 3 \times 3 = 2^3 \times 3^2$

- Numbers raised to the power of 2 are **squared**.

  Squares can be calculated using the $\boxed{x^2}$ button on a calculator.

  > **Square numbers** are whole numbers squared.
  > The first few square numbers are:   1,   4,   9,   16,   25,   36,   …

  The opposite of squaring a number is called finding the **square root**.

  Square roots can be calculated using the $\boxed{\sqrt{\phantom{x}}}$ button on a calculator.

  The square root of a number can be positive or negative.

  **Eg 7**   The square root of 9 can be written as $\sqrt{9}$ or $9^{\frac{1}{2}}$, and is equal to $+3$ or $-3$.

- Numbers raised to the power of 3 are **cubed**.

  > **Cube numbers** are whole numbers cubed.
  > The first few cube numbers are:   1,   8,   27,   64,   125,   …

  The opposite of cubing a number is called finding the **cube root**.

  Cube roots can be calculated using the $\boxed{\sqrt[3]{\phantom{x}}}$ button on a calculator.

  **Eg 8**   The cube root of 27 can be written as $\sqrt[3]{27}$ or $27^{\frac{1}{3}}$, and is equal to 3.

**(5)** ● **Powers**

The squares and cubes of numbers can be worked out on a calculator by using the $\boxed{x^y}$ button.

The $\boxed{x^y}$ button can be used to calculate the value of a number $x$ raised to the power of $y$.

**Eg 9**  Calculate $2.6^4$.
Enter the sequence: $\boxed{2}$ $\boxed{.}$ $\boxed{6}$ $\boxed{x^y}$ $\boxed{4}$ $\boxed{=}$  So,  $2.6^4 = 45.6976$.

● The **reciprocal** of a number is the value obtained when the number is divided into 1.

The reciprocal of a number can be found on a calculator by using the $\boxed{\frac{1}{x}}$ button.

> A number times its reciprocal equals 1.
> Zero has no reciprocal.
> The reciprocal of a number can be shown using an index of $-1$.

**Eg 10**  Find the reciprocal of 5.
The reciprocal of $5 = 5^{-1} = \frac{1}{5} = 0.2$

Using a calculator, press: $\boxed{5}$ $\boxed{\frac{1}{x}}$

● **Roots** can be calculated using the $\boxed{x^{1/y}}$ button.

**Eg 11**  Calculate $\sqrt[7]{128}$.
Enter the sequence: $\boxed{1}$ $\boxed{2}$ $\boxed{8}$ $\boxed{x^{1/y}}$ $\boxed{7}$ $\boxed{=}$  So,  $\sqrt[7]{128} = 2$.

● **The rules of indices**

| | |
|---|---|
| Multiplying powers with the same base | $a^m \times a^n = a^{m+n}$ |
| Dividing powers with the same base | $a^m \div a^n = a^{m-n}$ |
| Raising a power to a power | $(a^m)^n = a^{mn}$ |
| Raising any number to the power zero | $a^0 = 1$  (also $a^1 = a$) |
| Negative powers and reciprocals | $a^{-m} = \dfrac{1}{a^m}$  $a^{-m}$ is the reciprocal of $a^m$ |
| Fractional powers and roots | $a^{\frac{1}{n}} = \sqrt[n]{a}$  and  $a^{\frac{m}{n}} = \left(a^{\frac{1}{n}}\right)^m = \left(\sqrt[n]{a}\right)^m$ |

**Eg 12**  Simplify. Leave your answers in index form.
(a) $2^9 \times 2^4 = 2^{9+4} = 2^{13}$  (b) $2^9 \div 2^4 = 2^{9-4} = 2^5$  (c) $(4^9)^3 = 4^{9 \times 3} = 4^{27}$

● You should be able to use the function keys on a calculator to solve a variety of problems.

---

**Exercise 5**      Do not use a calculator for questions 1 to 17.

**1**  (a)  Write down all the factors of 18.
  (b)  Write down a multiple of 7 between 30 and 40.
  (c)  Explain why 15 is not a prime number.

**2**  A number of counters can be grouped into 2's, 3's, 4's and 5's.
  Find the smallest possible number of counters.

**3**  Look at these numbers.

| 2 | 15 | 27 | 36 | 44 | 51 | 64 |
|---|---|---|---|---|---|---|

  (a)  Which of these numbers is a prime number?
  (b)  Which of these numbers is both a square number and a cube number?

**4**  Richard says that  $1^3 + 2^3 = 3^3$.
  Is he right? Show your working.

**5**  Use examples to show that the sum of the squares of two prime numbers can be odd or even.

**6**  Find the value of  $\sqrt{(2 \times 2 \times 3 \times 3 \times 5 \times 5)}$.  *Edexcel*

**7**  Find the highest common factor of 108 and 180.  *Edexcel*

**8**
(a) Write 36 as a product of its prime factors.
(b) Write 45 as a product of its prime factors.
(c) What is the highest common factor of 36 and 45?
(d) What is the least common multiple of 36 and 45?

**9** A white light flashes every 10 seconds. A red light flashes every 6 seconds.
The two lights flash at the same time.
After how many seconds will the lights next flash at the same time?

**10** Work out. (a) $2^3 \times 3^2$ (b) $\left(\sqrt{9} \times \sqrt{25}\right)^2$ (c) $2^3 \times \sqrt[3]{64}$

**11**
(a) Which is smaller $\sqrt{225}$ or $2^4$? Show your working.
(b) Work out the value of $3^1 - 3^0 + 3^{-1}$.

**12** Find the value of $x$ in each of the following.
(a) $7^6 \times 7^3 = 7^x$ (b) $7^6 \div 7^3 = 7^x$ (c) $(7^6)^3 = 7^x$ (d) $7^0 = x$

**13** Write each of these expressions as a single power of 3. Leave your answers in power form.
(a) $3^{-2} \times 3^5$ (b) $3^4 \div 3^{-2}$ (c) $\dfrac{3^3 \times 3}{3^6}$

**14** $y = 2^{-x}$ Calculate the value of $y$ when (a) $x = 0$, (b) $x = 3$. *Edexcel*

**15** Evaluate: (a) $9^{\frac{1}{2}}$ (b) $64^{-\frac{1}{2}}$ (c) $25^{\frac{3}{2}}$ (d) $16^{-\frac{3}{4}}$

**16** Evaluate: $81^{0.5} \times 5^{-2}$. Give your answer as a fraction.

**17** Simplify, leaving your answers in fractional form.
(a) $64^{\frac{1}{2}} \times 125^{-\frac{1}{3}}$ (b) $27^{\frac{2}{3}} \times 3^{-4}$ (c) $\left(\frac{1}{2}\right)^{-3} \div \left(\frac{1}{5}\right)^{-2}$

**18** The number $x$ lies between 0 and 1.
(a) Write the following five expressions in order of size. Put the smallest one first.

$$x^2 \qquad \sqrt{x} \qquad x^3 \qquad \frac{1}{\sqrt{x}} \qquad x$$

The number $x$ and the number $y$ both lie between 0 and 1.
(b) For which of the following expressions could the value be greater than 1?

$$xy \qquad xy^2 \qquad (xy)^2 \qquad \frac{x}{y} \qquad \sqrt{\left(\frac{x}{y}\right)}$$

*Edexcel*

**19** Find the reciprocal of 7. Give your answer correct to two decimal places.

**20**
(a) Use your calculator to find the value of $5.43 \times \sqrt{(18 - 6.67)}$.
Write down all the figures on your calculator display.
(b) Give your answer to part (a) correct to 2 decimal places. *Edexcel*

**21** Use your calculator to find the value of $\sqrt{(47.3^2 - 9.1^2)}$.
(a) Write down all the figures on your calculator display.
(b) Write your answer to part (a) correct to 2 significant figures. *Edexcel*

**22** Use your calculator to work out the value of $\dfrac{\sqrt{12.3^2} + 7.9}{1.8 \times 0.17}$.
Give your answer correct to 1 decimal place. *Edexcel*

**23**
(a) Calculate the value of $\sqrt{\dfrac{4.1}{(0.19)^2}}$.
(b) Show how to check that your answer is of the right order of magnitude.

**24** Calculate the value of: (a) $5^{\frac{2}{5}}$ (b) $\dfrac{1}{(0.7)^5}$ (c) $\sqrt[3]{\dfrac{920\,000}{5^4}}$ (d) $\left(\dfrac{5.9}{\sqrt[3]{15}}\right)^{-3}$
Give your answers correct to two significant figures.

# Standard Index Form

## What you need to know

- **Standard index form**, or **standard form**, is a shorthand way of writing very large and very small numbers.

- In **standard form** a number is written as: **a number between 1 and 10 × a power of 10.**
  Large numbers (ten, or more) have a **positive** power of 10.

  **Eg 1**   Write   370 000   in standard form.
  $$370\,000 = 3.7 \times 100\,000 = 3.7 \times 10^5$$

  **Eg 2**   Write   $5.6 \times 10^7$   as an ordinary number.
  $$5.6 \times 10^7 = 5.6 \times 10\,000\,000 = 56\,000\,000$$

  Small positive numbers (less than one) have a **negative** power of 10.

  **Eg 3**   Write   0.000 73   in standard form.
  $$0.000\,73 = 7.3 \times 0.000\,1 = 7.3 \times 10^{-4}$$

  **Eg 4**   Write   $2.9 \times 10^{-6}$   as an ordinary number.
  $$2.9 \times 10^{-6} = 2.9 \times 0.000\,001 = 0.000\,002\,9$$

- You should be able to interpret the display on a calculator.

  **Eg 5**   The calculator display shows the answer to   $0.007 \times 0.09$
  In standard form, the answer is   $6.3 \times 10^{-4}$
  As an ordinary number, the answer is   0.000 63

  $$\boxed{6.3 \qquad -04}$$

- You should be able to solve problems involving numbers given in standard form.

## Exercise 6

Do not use a calculator for questions 1 to 9.

**1**   Write   one million   in standard form.

**2**   Look at these numbers.

$$\boxed{2.6 \times 10^4 \qquad 6.2 \times 10^3 \qquad 9.8 \times 10^{-4} \qquad 8.9 \times 10^{-5}}$$

   (a)   (i)   Which number is the largest?
         (ii)   Write your answer as an ordinary number.
   (b)   (i)   Which number is the smallest?
         (ii)   Write your answer as an ordinary number.

**3**   (a)   Write   0.053   in standard form.
    (b)   Write   $672 \times 10^8$   in standard form.      Edexcel

**4**   Work out.
   (a)   $(6 \times 10^3) + (5 \times 10^4)$
   (b)   $(6 \times 10^3) \times (5 \times 10^4)$
   (c)   $(6 \times 10^3) \div (5 \times 10^4)$
   Give your answers in standard form.

**5**   Work out   $4 \times 10^8 - 4 \times 10^6$.
   Give your answer in standard form.      Edexcel

**6**   The mass of an atom of oxygen is 0.000 000 000 000 000 000 000 027 grams.
   (a)   Write this number in standard form.
   (b)   Calculate, in standard form, the mass of $5 \times 10^8$ atoms of oxygen.      Edexcel

**7** The table shows the populations of four countries in Latin America.

| Country | Population |
|---------|-----------|
| Belize | $2.0 \times 10^5$ |
| Guatemala | $1.2 \times 10^7$ |
| Mexico | $1.1 \times 10^8$ |
| Nicaragua | $4.9 \times 10^6$ |

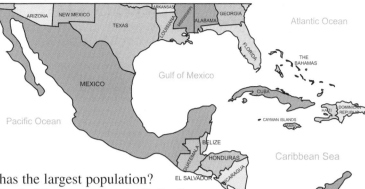

(a) Which of these countries has the largest population?
(b) How many more people live in Nicaragua than in Belize?
(c) What is the total population of these four countries?
Give your answer in standard form.

**8** A spaceship travelled for $6 \times 10^2$ hours at a speed of $8 \times 10^4$ km/h.
(a) Calculate the distance travelled by the spaceship.
Give your answer in standard form.

One month an aircraft travelled $2 \times 10^5$ km.
The next month the aircraft travelled $3 \times 10^4$ km.
(b) Calculate the total distance travelled by the aircraft in the two months.
Give your answer as an ordinary number.

*Edexcel*

**9** Work out $\dfrac{3 \times 10^4}{5 \times 10^{-5}}$ giving your answer in standard form.

**10** The mass of a neutron is $1.675 \times 10^{-24}$ grams.
Calculate the total mass of 1500 neutrons.
Give your answer in standard form.

*Edexcel*

**11** (a) Calculate $\dfrac{7.2 \times 10^6}{0.0045}$
Give your answer in standard form.

(b) Calculate $\dfrac{530}{6.7 \times 10^5}$
Give your answer as an ordinary number correct to two significant figures.

**12** In Astronomy, the distance between stars is measured in light years.
A light year is approximately $9.46 \times 10^{12}$ kilometres.
Alpha Cygni is approximately $1.05 \times 10^{14}$ kilometres from the Sun.
How many light years is Alpha Cygni from the Sun?

**13** The volume of Elspeth's house is 379.6m³.
(a) Write 379.6 in standard form.

The heat, $H$, needed to keep a house warm is given by the formula
$$H = \frac{5544 \times 1.4 \times 3 \times 22.5 \times \text{Volume of house}}{2000}$$

(b) Calculate the value of $H$ for Elspeth's house, giving your answer in standard form.

*Edexcel*

**14** Work out $\dfrac{3.5 \times 10^{-3}}{4.1 \times 10^2}$

Give your answer as an ordinary number correct to 2 significant figures.

**15** Work out $\dfrac{(3.5 \times 10^6) \times (5 \times 10^{-4})}{2.5 \times 10^5}$
Give your answer as an ordinary number.

# Ratio and Proportion ● ● ● ● ●

## What you need to know

- The ratio 3 : 2 is read '3 to 2'.

- A ratio is used only to **compare** quantities.
  A ratio does not give information about the exact values of quantities being compared.

- In its **simplest form**, a ratio contains whole numbers which have no common factor other than 1.

  **Eg 1**  Write £2.40 : 40p in its simplest form.
  £2.40 : 40p = 240p : 40p
  $\qquad\qquad$ = 240 : 40
  $\qquad\qquad$ = 6 : 1

  > All quantities in a ratio must be in the **same units** before the ratio can be simplified.

- You should be able to solve a variety of problems involving ratio.

  **Eg 2**  The ratio of bats to balls in a box is 3 : 5.
  There are 12 bats in the box.
  How many balls are there?

  12 ÷ 3 = 4
  3 × 4 : 5 × 4 = 12 : 20
  There are 20 balls in the box.

  > For every 3 bats there are 5 balls.
  > To find an **equivalent ratio** to 3 : 5, in which the first number is 12, multiply each number in the ratio by 4.

  **Eg 3**  A wall costs £660 to build.
  The costs of materials to labour are in the ratio 4 : 7.
  What is the cost of labour?

  4 + 7 = 11
  £660 ÷ 11 = £60
  Cost of labour = £60 × 7 = £420

  > The numbers in the ratio add to 11.
  > For every £11 of the total cost, £4 pays for materials and £7 pays for labour.
  > So, **divide** by 11 and then **multiply** by 7.

- When two different quantities are always in the **same ratio** the two quantities are in **direct proportion**.

  **Eg 4**  20 litres of petrol cost £14.
  Find the cost of 25 litres of petrol.

  20 litres cost £14
  1 litre costs £14 ÷ 20 = £0.70
  25 litres cost £0.70 × 25 = £17.50

  > This is sometimes called the **unitary method**.
  > **Divide** by 20 to find the cost of 1 litre.
  > **Multiply** by 25 to find the cost of 25 litres.

- When as one quantity increases the other decreases, the quantities are in **inverse proportion**.

  **Eg 5**  3 people take 8 hours to deliver some leaflets.
  How long would it take 4 people?

  3 people take 8 hours.
  1 person takes 8 hours × 3 = 24 hours
  4 people take 24 hours ÷ 4 = 6 hours
  So, 4 people would take 6 hours.

  > This assumes that time is **inversely proportional** to the number of people.
  > **Multiply** by 3 to find how long 1 person would take.
  > **Divide** by 4 to find how long 4 people would take.

## Exercise 7

Do not use a calculator for questions 1 to 6.

1  A toy box contains large bricks and small bricks in the ratio 1 : 4.
   The box contains 40 bricks. How many large bricks are in the box?

**2** To make mortar a builder mixes sand and cement in the ratio 3 : 1.
The builder uses 2.5 kg of cement. How much sand does he use?

**3** In a drama club the ratio of boys to girls is 2 : 3.
(a)    What fraction of club members are girls?
(b)    What percentage of club members are boys?

**4** The ratio of men to women playing golf one day is 5 : 3.
There are 20 men playing. How many women are playing?

**5** Rashid has 35 sweets.
He shares them in the ratio 4 : 3 with his sister.
Rashid keeps the larger share.
How many sweets does Rashid keep?

Edexcel

**6** Dec shares a prize of £435 with Annabel in the ratio 3 : 2.
What is the difference in the amount of money they each receive?

**7** To make 20 m³ of concrete for a building, the builders use:
$$4 \text{ m}^3 \text{ of cement, } 12 \text{ m}^3 \text{ of sand and } 4 \text{ m}^3 \text{ of ballast.}$$
(a)    What is the ratio of cement to sand? Give your answer in its lowest terms.
(b)    How much cement would be needed for 100 m³ of concrete?

Edexcel

**8** A bag contains red counters and white counters in the ratio 3 : 5.
Six red counters are taken from the bag.
The ratio of red counters to white counters left in the bag is 1 : 5.
How many counters are left in the bag?

**9** Two students are talking about their school outing.

My class went to Tower Bridge last week.
There are 30 people in my class.
The total cost was £345.

There are 45 people in my group.
What will be the total cost for my group?

**10**

Three 1-litre tins of paint cost a total of £26.85.
Find the cost of five of the 1-litre tins of paint.

Edexcel

**11** A farmer estimates it will take 2 combine harvesters 6 days to harvest his crop.
Estimate how many days it will take 3 combine harvesters to harvest his crop.

**12** When petrol is 80 pence a litre it costs £28.80 to fill the tank of my car with petrol.
How much will it cost to fill the tank of my car with petrol when petrol is 90 pence per litre?

**13** On a map the distance between two towns is 5 cm.
The actual distance between the towns is 1 kilometre.
What is the scale of the map in the form of 1 : $n$?

**14** Malika's father won £128.
He shared the £128 between his three children in the ratio 6 : 3 : 1.
(a)    Malika was given the biggest share. Work out how much money Malika received.
(b)    Malika saved $\frac{2}{3}$ of her share. Work out how much Malika saved.

Edexcel

**15** At 80 km/h it takes 30 minutes to complete a journey.
How long would it take to complete the journey at 50 km/h?

# Speed and Other Compound Measures

## What you need to know

- **Speed** is a compound measure because it involves **two** other measures.

- **Speed** is a measurement of how fast something is travelling.
  It involves two other measures, **distance** and **time**.
  In situations where speed is not constant, **average speed** is used.

  | The formula linking speed, distance and time can be rearranged and remembered as: |
  | $S = D \div T$ |
  | $D = S \times T$ |
  | $T = D \div S$ |

  $$\text{Speed} = \frac{\text{Distance}}{\text{Time}} \qquad \text{Average speed} = \frac{\text{Total distance travelled}}{\text{Total time taken}}$$

- You should be able to solve problems involving speed, distance and time.

  **Eg 1** A greyhound takes 32 seconds to run 400 metres.
  Calculate its speed in metres per second.

  $$\text{Speed} = \frac{\text{Distance}}{\text{Time}} = \frac{400}{32} = 12.5 \text{ metres per second}$$

  **Eg 2** Norrie says, "If I drive at an average speed of 60 km/h it will take me $2\frac{1}{2}$ hours to complete my journey." What distance is his journey?

  $$\text{Distance} = \text{Speed} \times \text{Time} = 60 \times 2\frac{1}{2} = 150 \text{ km}$$

  **Eg 3** Ellen cycles 5 km at an average speed of 12 km/h.
  How many minutes does she take?

  To change hours to minutes:
  **multiply by 60**

  $$\text{Time} = \frac{\text{Distance}}{\text{Speed}} = \frac{5}{12} \text{ hours} = \frac{5}{12} \times 60 = 25 \text{ minutes}$$

- **Density** is a compound measure which involves the measures **mass** and **volume**.

  **Eg 4** A block of metal has mass 500 g and volume 400 cm³.

  $$\text{Density} = \frac{\text{Mass}}{\text{Volume}} = \frac{500}{400} = 1.25 \text{ g/cm}^3$$

  $$\text{Density} = \frac{\text{Mass}}{\text{Volume}}$$

- **Population density** is a measure of how populated an area is.

  **Eg 5** The population of Cumbria is 489 700.
  The area of Cumbria is 6824 km².

  $$\text{Population density} = \frac{\text{Population}}{\text{Area}}$$

  $$\text{Population density} = \frac{\text{Population}}{\text{Area}} = \frac{489\ 700}{6824} = 71.8 \text{ people/km}^2.$$

## Exercise 8

Do not use a calculator for questions 1 to 4.

1. Marcus cycled 18 km at an average speed of 15 km/h.
   How long did he take to complete the journey? Give your answer in hours and minutes.

2. A motorist travels a distance of 156 miles in $3\frac{1}{4}$ hours.
   Calculate the average speed of the motorist in miles per hour.

3. Gail leaves home at 0950 to walk to the park.
   She walks at an average speed of 5 km/h and reaches the park at 1020.
   How far is the park from her home?

4. Kay walks 2.7 km in 45 minutes.
   Calculate her average walking speed in kilometres per hour.

**5** In the College Games, Michael Jackson won the 200 metres race in a time of 20.32 seconds.
Calculate his average speed in metres per second.
Give your answer correct to 1 decimal place.

Edexcel

**6** Mia drove a distance of 343 km. She took 3 hours 30 minutes.
Work our her average speed. Give your answer in km/h.

Edexcel

**7** The diagram shows the distances, in miles, between some junctions on a motorway.

West ← ——(25)—— **12** ——(26)—— **8** ——(27)—— → East

A coach is travelling west. At 1040 it passes junction 27 and at 1052 it passes junction 26.
(a) Calculate the average speed of the coach in miles per hour.

Between junctions 26 and 25 the coach travels at an average speed of 30 miles per hour.
(b) Calculate the time when the coach passes junction 25.

**8** A train travels at an average speed of 80 miles per hour.
At 0940 the train is 65 miles from Glasgow. The train is due to arrive in Glasgow at 1030.
Will it arrive on time? Show your working.

**9** A horse gallops at an average speed of 24 km/h for $4\frac{1}{2}$ minutes.
Calculate the distance it travels.

**10** On Monday it took Helen 40 minutes to drive to work.
On Tuesday it took Helen 25 minutes to drive to work.
Her average speed on Monday was 18 miles per hour.
What was her average speed on Tuesday?

**11** Rhys completed a 400 m race in 64 seconds.
Calculate his average speed in kilometres per hour.

**12** A jet-ski travels 0.9 kilometres in 1.5 minutes.
Calculate the average speed of the jet-ski in metres per second.

**13** The distance from the Earth to the Moon is $3.81 \times 10^5$ kilometres.
Light travels at a speed of $3 \times 10^8$ metres per second.
How long does it take light to travel from the Earth to the Moon?

**14** (a) A goods train, 150 metres long, is travelling at 45 km/h.
How many seconds does it take to pass a signal?
(b) The goods train takes 5 seconds to pass a passenger train, 90 metres long,
travelling in the opposite direction.
Calculate the speed of the passenger train in kilometres per hour.

**15** A copper statue has a mass of 1080 g and a volume of 120 cm³.
Work out the density of copper.

**16** A silver medal has a mass of 200 g. The density of silver is 10.5 g/cm³.
What is the volume of the medal?

**17** The population of Jamaica is 2.8 million people. The area of Jamaica is 10 800 km².
What is the population density of Jamaica?

**18** The table gives some information about North America.

| Country | Area (km²) | Population | Population density (people/km²) |
|---|---|---|---|
| Canada | 9 860 000 | | 2.98 |
| United States | | $2.68 \times 10^8$ | 28.9 |

Calculate   (a)   the population of Canada,        (b)   the area of the United States.

# Extending the Number System

**What you need to know**

- **Rational numbers** can be written in the form $\frac{a}{b}$, where $a$ and $b$ are integers ($b \neq 0$).

  Examples of rational numbers are: $2$, $-5$, $\frac{2}{5}$, $0.6$, $3.47$, $1\frac{3}{4}$.

- All fractions can be written as decimals.

  For example, $\frac{1}{3} = 0.3333333... = 0.\dot{3}$, $\frac{123}{999} = 0.123123123... = 0.\dot{1}2\dot{3}$

- You should be able to convert a recurring decimal to a fraction.

  **Eg 1**  Find the fraction which is equal to $0.\dot{2}\dot{7}$, in its simplest form.

  | |
  |---|
  | $x = 0.2727...$ <br> 2 digits recur, so, multiply by 100. <br> $100x = 27.2727...$ <br> $99x = 27$ <br> $x = \frac{27}{99} = \frac{3}{11}$ <br> $0.\dot{2}\dot{7} = \frac{3}{11}$ |

  > Let $x$ = the recurring decimal.
  > Multiply both sides by a power of 10:
  > - by $10^1 = 10$ if only 1 digit recurs,
  > - by $10^2 = 100$ if 2 digits recur, and so on.
  >
  > Subtract the original equation from the new equation.
  > Solve the resulting equation for $x$.
  > If necessary, write the fraction in its simplest form.

- All **terminating** and **recurring decimals** are rational numbers.

- A **surd** is the root of a rational number which is not rational.
  A surd is an **irrational number**.

  These are examples of surds: $\sqrt{2}$   $\sqrt{0.37}$   $3 + \sqrt{2}$

  $\sqrt{9}$ is not a surd because   $\sqrt{9} = 3$   which is rational.

  > $\sqrt{a}$ means the positive square root of $a$.

- Rules for manipulating and simplifying surds:

  $$\sqrt{ab} = \sqrt{a} \times \sqrt{b} \qquad m\sqrt{a} + n\sqrt{a} = (m + n)\sqrt{a} \qquad \sqrt{\frac{a}{b}} = \frac{\sqrt{a}}{\sqrt{b}}$$

  **Eg 2**  Simplify the following leaving the answers in surd form.

  (a)  $\sqrt{32} = \sqrt{16} \times \sqrt{2} = 4\sqrt{2}$     > Look for factors that are square numbers.

  (b)  $\sqrt{8} + \sqrt{18} = \sqrt{4} \times \sqrt{2} + \sqrt{9} \times \sqrt{2} = 2\sqrt{2} + 3\sqrt{2} = 5\sqrt{2}$

  (c)  $\sqrt{\frac{72}{20}} = \frac{\sqrt{72}}{\sqrt{20}} = \frac{\sqrt{36}\sqrt{2}}{\sqrt{4}\sqrt{5}} = \frac{6\sqrt{2}}{2\sqrt{5}} = \frac{3\sqrt{2}}{\sqrt{5}}$

- To **rationalise** the denominator of a fraction of the form $\frac{a}{\sqrt{b}}$ multiply both the numerator (top) and the denominator (bottom) of the fraction by $\sqrt{b}$.

  **Eg 3**  Rationalise the denominator and simplify where possible:  $\frac{3\sqrt{2}}{6}$.

  $$\frac{3\sqrt{2}}{\sqrt{6}} = \frac{3\sqrt{2}}{\sqrt{6}} \times \frac{\sqrt{6}}{\sqrt{6}} = \frac{3\sqrt{2}\sqrt{6}}{6} = \frac{3\sqrt{2}\sqrt{2}\sqrt{3}}{6} = \frac{6\sqrt{3}}{6} = \sqrt{3}$$

- You should be able to use surds in calculations.

  > To keep an answer exact it is necessary to keep numbers like $\sqrt{3}$ in surd form.

Do not use a calculator for this exercise.

**1** (a) Change $\frac{5}{7}$ into a decimal.

(b) Find the fraction which is equal to $0.\dot{2}$.
Give your answer in its simplest terms.

**2** Simplify. (a) $2\sqrt{5} + 3\sqrt{5}$ (b) $\sqrt{3} \times \sqrt{3}$ (c) $\sqrt{2} \times \sqrt{3} \times \sqrt{6}$ (d) $\sqrt{\frac{9}{16}}$

**3** (a) Prove that $0.4\dot{5} = \frac{5}{11}$.

(b) Write the number $0.\dot{6}\dot{3}$ as a fraction in its simplest form.

**4** Write the recurring decimal $0.4\dot{8}$ in the form $\frac{a}{b}$, where $a$ and $b$ are integers. Edexcel

**5** (a) Express 12 as the product of its prime factors.

(b) $\sqrt{12}$ can be written in the form of $a\sqrt{b}$ where $a$ and $b$ are prime numbers.
Calculate the values of $a$ and $b$.

**6** Write $\sqrt{18}$ in the form of $a\sqrt{b}$ where $a$ and $b$ are prime numbers.

**7** Simplify, leaving your answers where appropriate in surd form.

(a) $5\sqrt{3} - \sqrt{3}$ (b) $\sqrt{3} \times 3\sqrt{3}$ (c) $\frac{\sqrt{27}}{3}$ (d) $\sqrt{12} \times \sqrt{75}$

**8** Simplify fully.

(a) $\sqrt{45}$ (b) $\sqrt{45} + \sqrt{20}$ (c) $\frac{\sqrt{45}}{\sqrt{20}}$ (d) $\left(\sqrt{45} - \sqrt{20}\right)^2$

**9** Simplify the expression $\sqrt{24}\left(\sqrt{50} - \sqrt{8}\right)$.

**10** Express each of the following in its simplest form with a rational denominator.

(a) $\frac{6}{\sqrt{3}}$ (b) $\frac{15}{2\sqrt{5}}$

**11** The area of this rectangle is 81 cm². 
Work out the value of $k$.

$3^k$ cm
$\sqrt{3}$ cm

Edexcel

**12** (a) Given that $\sqrt{75} = k\sqrt{3}$, find the value of $k$.

(b) Rationalise the denominator of $\frac{18}{\sqrt{3}}$ and simplify your answer.

**13** (a) Find the value of (i) $m$ when $\sqrt{128} = 2^m$, (ii) $n$ when $\left(\sqrt{8} - \sqrt{2}\right)^2 = 2^n$.

A rectangle has a length of $2^t$ cm and a width of $\left(\sqrt{8} - \sqrt{2}\right)$ cm.
The area of the rectangle is $\sqrt{128}$ cm².
(b) Find $t$. Edexcel

**14** A large rectangular piece of card is $\left(\sqrt{5} + \sqrt{20}\right)$ cm long and $\sqrt{8}$ cm wide.

A small rectangle, $\sqrt{2}$ cm long and $\sqrt{5}$ cm wide, is cut out of the piece of card.

Express the area of the card that is left as a percentage of the large rectangle. Edexcel

**15** You are given that $a = \sqrt{5} + 3$ and $b = \sqrt{5} - 3$.

(a) $a + b = \sqrt{n}$. Find the value of $n$.

(b) Find the value of $\frac{a - b}{ab}$.

# Number
# Non-calculator Paper

Do not use a calculator for this exercise.

**1** Use these numbers to answer the following questions.

$$3 \quad 7 \quad 11 \quad 15 \quad 19 \quad 23 \quad 27$$

(a) Which number in the list is a factor of another number in the list?

(b) Which number is a cube number?

(c) (i) Which numbers are not prime numbers? Give a reason for your answer.

(ii) The numbers are part of a sequence.
What is the next number in the sequence which is not a prime number?

**2** Using the information that $97 \times 123 = 11\,931$, write down the value of

(a) $9.7 \times 12.3$      (b) $0.97 \times 123\,000$      (c) $11.931 \div 9.7$      Edexcel

**3** (a) Work out. (i) $5 - 0.26$      (ii) $0.2 \times 0.4$      (iii) $24 \div 0.3$

(b) A turkey costs £3.60 per kilogram.
What is the cost of a turkey which weighs 6.5 kilograms?

**4** (a) Write these fractions in order, smallest first: $\frac{1}{2}$   $\frac{2}{3}$   $\frac{3}{5}$   $\frac{5}{8}$   $\frac{3}{4}$

(b) Write down a fraction that lies halfway between $\frac{1}{5}$ and $\frac{1}{4}$.

(c) Work out (i) $\frac{1}{4} + \frac{2}{5}$,      (ii) $\frac{2}{3} - \frac{1}{2}$,      (iii) $\frac{4}{5} \times \frac{2}{3}$.

**5** On average, Nick walks 18 000 steps every day.
He walks 1 mile approximately every 3500 steps.
Work out an estimate for the average distance, in miles, that Nick walks **in one year**.      Edexcel

**6** A box contains 500 screws, to the nearest 10.
What is the smallest and largest possible number of screws in the box?

**7** Three cups of tea cost £2.85. How much will five cups of tea cost?

**8** It costs £1.20 to buy a melon on Tuesday. On Wednesday it costs 15% **more**.
How much does it cost to buy a melon on Wednesday?

**9** (a) Conrad cycles 24 km in $1\frac{1}{2}$ hours. What is his cycling speed in kilometres per hour?

(b) Cas cycles 24 km at 15 km/h. She sets off at 0930. At what time does she finish?

**10** Work out (a) $\frac{2}{5} + \frac{3}{8}$,      (b) $5\frac{2}{3} - 2\frac{3}{4}$.      Edexcel

**11** A crowd of 54 000 people watch a carnival.
$\frac{2}{3}$ of the crowd are children and $\frac{3}{5}$ of the children are girls.
What percentage of the crowd are girls?

**12** The prime factors of a certain number are $2^3 \times 3 \times 11$. What is the number?      Edexcel

**13** Write $\dfrac{5^3 \times 5^3}{5^2}$ as a single power of 5.

**14** Jack shares £180 between his two children Ruth and Ben.
The ratio of Ruth's share to Ben's share is 5 : 4.

(a) Work out how much each child is given.

Ben then gives 10% of his share to Ruth.

(b) Work out the percentage of the £180 that Ruth now has.      Edexcel

**15** (a) Write as a product of its prime factors: (i) 72, (ii) 96.

(b) Hence, find the least common multiple of 72 and 96.

**16** (a) Write these numbers in standard form. (i) 38 600 000 (ii) 0.000 054

(b) Calculate (i) $5 \times 10^5$ times $2 \times 10^3$, (ii) $(2 \times 10^3) \div (5 \times 10^5)$.
Give your answers in standard form.

**17** Work out an estimate for the value of $\dfrac{29.91 - 2 \times 10.03}{29.91^2 - 10.03^2}$.

Give your answer as a fraction in its simplest form. *Edexcel*

**18** Work out. (a) $1\frac{1}{4} \times 2\frac{2}{3}$ (b) $2\frac{1}{2} \div 1\frac{2}{3}$

**19** Two cucumbers and three lettuces cost £2.64.
A cucumber costs 25% more than a lettuce. Find the cost of a cucumber.

**20** Felix and Jan are in cars travelling in opposite directions along a motorway.
At 1015 they are 30 km apart and travelling towards each other.
Felix is travelling at an average speed of 70 km/h.
If they pass each other at 1027, what is Jan's average speed?

**21** The ratio of male to female passengers on a bus is 3 : 5.
At the next stop 5 females get off and 2 males get on.
The ratio of male to female passengers is now 4 : 5.
How many male passengers are now on the bus?

**22** The number $10^{100}$ is called a googol.

(a) Write the number 50 googols in standard index form.

A nanometre is $10^{-9}$ metres.

(b) Write 50 nanometres, in metres. Give your answer in standard index form. *Edexcel*

**23** In a sale all the prices are reduced by 30%. The sale price of a jacket is £28.
Work out the price of the jacket before the sale. *Edexcel*

**24** (a) Write 240 as the product of its prime factors.

(b) Hence, find the smallest whole number 240 must be multiplied by to give a perfect square.

**25** It takes 15 minutes to fill a paddling pool at the rate of 12 litres per minute.
How long will it take to fill the pool at the rate of 20 litres per minute?

**26** (a) Express $81^{-\frac{1}{2}}$ as a fraction in the form $\frac{a}{b}$ where $a$ and $b$ are integers.

(b) Find the value of $y$ for which $2 \times 4^y = 64$. *Edexcel*

**27** (a) What is the reciprocal of 2.5?

(b) Write these numbers in descending order. $5^{-1}$ $\left(\frac{1}{4}\right)^{\frac{1}{2}}$ $2^{-3}$ $3^{-2}$ $\left(\frac{1}{2}\right)^2$

(c) Find the value of $x$ when:
(i) $2^4 \times 2^3 = 2^x$, (ii) $3^{-2} \div 3^{-4} = 3^x$, (iii) $216^{\frac{1}{3}} = 6^x$.

(d) Work out $9^{-\frac{3}{2}}$. Give your answer as a fraction.

**28** A jug holds 4.6 litres of milk, correct to one decimal place.
Write down the lower and upper bounds of the amount of milk in the jug.

**29** (a) (i) Simplify the following expression, leaving your answer in surd form. $\sqrt{27} + \sqrt{75}$

(ii) **Hence**, simplify the expression $\dfrac{\sqrt{27} + \sqrt{75}}{\sqrt{12}}$.

(b) Calculate $64^{\frac{2}{3}}$.

(c) Calculate $27^{-\frac{1}{3}}$, giving your answer as a fraction.

(d) Write the number $0.\overset{..}{2}\overset{.}{1}$ as a fraction in its simplest form.

You may use a calculator for this exercise.

**1**

**DISCO'S JEANS**
Normal Price
£36
*SALE PRICE*
$\frac{2}{3}$ **Normal Price**

Bob's Cut Price
JEANS
Normal Price £30
*SALE:- 15% off*

SANJAY'S MARKET
*JEANS*
£22 + 17.5% V.A.T.

Frances sees three different advertisements for jeans.
Work out the cost of the jeans in each advertisement.                Edexcel

**2** Jacob is 3.7 kg heavier than Isaac. The sum of their weights is 44.5 kg. How heavy is Jacob?

**3** To make squash, orange juice and water is mixed in the ratio of 1 : 6.
How much orange juice is needed to make 35 litres of squash?

**4** Wayne invited 96 people to an engagement party.
Only 60 of the people invited came to the party.
Express 60 as a percentage of 96.                Edexcel

**5** Work out the value of $\sqrt{46} - 2.5^2$, correct to one significant figure.                Edexcel

**6** Cheri is paid a basic rate of £6.40 per hour for a 35-hour week.
Overtime is paid at $1\frac{1}{2}$ times the basic rate. Last week she was paid £262.40.
How many hours did Cheri work last week?

**7** Find the **simple** interest on £3500 invested for 3 years at 4% per year.                Edexcel

**8** The diagram shows the weights and prices of two packets of gravy granules.
This week both packets are on special offer.
The smaller packet has one third off the normal price.
The larger packet has 30% off the normal price.
Which packet is better value this week?
Show your working.

Gravy Granules
180 g
Normal price
54p

Gravy Granules
300 g
Normal price
90p

**9** Harvey lives 3 kilometres from school.
He walks to school at an average speed of 5 km/h.
The school day starts at 0900.
What is the latest time Harvey can leave home and still get to school on time?

**10** Evaluate $\dfrac{(23.4 + 35.6) \times 5.7}{200.3 \times (16.2 - 8.15)}$.                Edexcel

**11** There are 12 inches in 1 foot. There are 3 feet in 1 yard. There are 2.54 centimetres in 1 inch.
Express 1 metre in yards. Give your answer correct to 3 decimal places.                Edexcel

**12** Verity and Jean share £126 in the ratio 5 : 3.
Work out how much money Verity receives.                Edexcel

**13** A caravan is for sale at £7200. Stuart buys the caravan on credit.
The credit terms are:

> deposit 25% of sale price and 36 monthly payments of £175.

FOR SALE
£7200

Express the extra amount paid for credit, compared with the cash price,
as a percentage of the cash price.

**14** (a) Express 108 as the product of powers of its prime factors.
(b) Find the highest common factor of 108 and 24.

Edexcel

**15** In England, a jar of **extra fruity** apricot jam weighs 454 g and costs 89p.
In France, a jar of **extra fruity** apricot jam weighs 681 g and costs 1.84 euros.
    £1 = 1.58 euros.
In which country is the jam better value for money? You must show all your working.

**16** (a) Write the following fractions as decimals, writing all the figures shown on your calculator.
    (i) $\frac{9}{10}$    (ii) $\frac{45}{51}$
(b) Work out a fraction that is between $\frac{9}{10}$ and $\frac{45}{51}$ in size.

Edexcel

**17** (a) What is the reciprocal of 0.35?   Give your answer correct to two decimal places.

(b) Work out $\frac{3.2^2}{\sqrt{0.04}}$.

**18** In 2004, Ashley's council tax bill was £965.40.
In 2005, Ashley's council tax bill was 6.8% more than in 2004.
In 2006, Ashley's council tax bill was 4.9% more than in 2005.
(a) Calculate Ashley's council tax bill in 2006.
    Give your answer to a suitable degree of accuracy.
(b) Calculate the percentage increase in council tax between 2004 and 2006.

**19** Karina says,

  *"For some numbers the square root of the number is larger than the number itself."*
For what numbers is this true?

**20** At 20 miles per hour a bus journey takes 40 minutes.
A taxi does the same journey at 25 miles per hour.
How many minutes does the taxi take?

**21** A shop buys Indian rugs from a factory.
In July, the cost to the shop of buying a rug was £100.
The shop bought 800 rugs in July.
In August, the cost to the shop of buying a rug increased by 10%.
The number of rugs bought by the shop decreased by 25%.
Find the difference between the total cost to the shop of all the rugs bought in July and the
total cost of all the rugs bought by the shop in August.

Edexcel

**22** £1 can buy 1.54 euros.   £1 can buy 1.37 dollars.
How many dollars can be bought with 1000 euros?

**23** (a) Place the following numbers in order, largest first:   $\sqrt{6.9}$    2.58    $1.6^2$    $2\frac{4}{7}$

(b) (i) Calculate $\frac{612 \times 29.6}{81.3 - 18.9}$.

    (ii) Use approximations to show that your answer is about right. Show your working.

**24** In 2005, the population of the World was estimated to be 6700 million.
If the population increases at the rate of 1.7% per year, estimate the population of the World
in 2010.
Give your answer correct to 3 significant figures.

**25** The selling price of a computer is
the **list price** plus VAT at $17\frac{1}{2}\%$.

The selling price of a computer is £1292.50.
Work out the **list price** of this computer.

Selling price =
list price +
VAT

Edexcel

**26** $p = 3^2 \times 5 \times 7$ and $q = 2 \times 3 \times 5^2$. Find the least common multiple of $p$ and $q$.

**27** The population of China is $1.2 \times 10^9$. The area of China is $9.5 \times 10^6$ square kilometres. What is the population density of China?

**28** (a) You are given the formula $k = \frac{3}{4} m^2$.
Calculate the exact value of $k$, when $m = 4.8 \times 10^3$.
Give your answer in standard form.

(b) Calculate $\sqrt{\dfrac{5.2 \times 10^{-3}}{(0.039)^2}}$ correct to two decimal places.

**29** (a) Jools invests £2000 at 6.5% per annum compound interest.
Calculate the value of his investment at the end of 3 years.

(b) Jennifer gets 6% per annum on her investment.
After one year the value of her investment is £1272.
How much did she invest?

**30** Last year Alf had a tax allowance of £4895 and paid £4697 in tax. The rates of tax were:

> 10p in the £ on the first £2090 of taxable income and
> 22p in the £ on all the remaining taxable income.

How much did Alf earn last year?

**31** Calculate the value of $\dfrac{5.98 \times 10^8 + 4.32 \times 10^9}{6.14 \times 10^{-2}}$.

Give your answer in standard form correct to 3 significant figures.  Edexcel

**32** A company bought a new truck. Each year the value of the truck depreciates by 20%.
The value of the new truck can be multiplied by a single number to find its value at the end of four years.
Find this single number as a decimal.  Edexcel

**33** A greengrocer buys apples and resells them at a profit of 12%.
How much did the greengrocer pay for apples which are sold for 84 pence?

**34** Write the recurring decimal 0.353535… as a fraction in the form $\frac{x}{y}$, where $x$ and $y$ are integers.  Edexcel

**35** The land area of France is $5.41 \times 10^5$ square kilometres.
The land area of the Earth is $1.32 \times 10^8$ square kilometres.
Calculate the land area of France as a percentage of the land area of the Earth.
Give your answer to a suitable degree of accuracy.

**36** (a) Write $\sqrt{45}$ in the form $a\sqrt{b}$ where $a$ and $b$ are prime numbers.

(b) Write $\dfrac{5}{\sqrt{10}}$ in the form $\dfrac{\sqrt{a}}{b}$ where $a$ and $b$ are whole numbers.

(c) Express $\sqrt{32}$ as a power of 2.

(d) Simplify $4^0 + 4^{-1} + 4^{-2}$.

(e) Write $0.\dot{2}\dot{7}$ as a fraction in its simplest form.

**37** Calculate the value of $(5.8 \times 10^{-5})^{\frac{1}{3}}$.
Give your answer in standard form correct to 2 significant figures.

**38** (a) Write $0.0\dot{4}$ as a fraction in its simplest form.

(b) Simplify (i) $\sqrt{12} + \sqrt{75}$    (ii) $\sqrt{12} \times \sqrt{75}$

(c) Rationalise $\dfrac{\sqrt{27} - \sqrt{12}}{\sqrt{15}}$.

# Introduction to Algebra ● ● ● ●

## What you need to know

- You should be able to write **algebraic expressions**.

  **Eg 1** An expression for the cost of 6 pens at $n$ pence each is $6n$ pence.

  **Eg 2** An expression for 2 pence more than $n$ pence is $n + 2$ pence.

- Be able to **simplify expressions** by collecting **like terms** together.

  **Eg 3** (a) $2d + 3d = 5d$ (b) $3x + 2 - x + 4 = 2x + 6$ (c) $x + 2x + x^2 = 3x + x^2$

- Be able to **multiply expressions** together.

  **Eg 4** (a) $2a \times a = 2a^2$ (b) $y \times y \times y = y^3$ (c) $3m \times 2n = 6mn$

- Be able to recall and use these properties of powers:
  Powers of the same base are **added** when terms are **multiplied**.
  Powers of the same base are **subtracted** when terms are **divided**.
  Powers are **multiplied** when a power is raised to a power.

  $$a^m \times a^n = a^{m+n}$$
  $$a^m \div a^n = a^{m-n}$$
  $$(a^m)^n = a^{m \times n}$$

  **Eg 5** (a) $x^3 \times x^2 = x^5$ (b) $a^5 \div a^2 = a^3$ (c) $6m^6 \div 2m^2 = 3m^4$ (d) $(2y^2)^3 = 8y^6$

- Be able to **multiply out brackets**.

  **Eg 6** (a) $2(x - 5) = 2x - 10$ (b) $x(x - 5) = x^2 - 5x$ (c) $2m(m + 3) = 2m^2 + 6m$

- Be able to **factorise expressions**.

  **Eg 7** (a) $3x - 6 = 3(x - 2)$ (b) $m^2 + 5m = m(m + 5)$ (c) $3a^2 - 6a = 3a(a - 2)$

## Exercise 10

**1** Godfrey is 5 years older than Mary.
Write expressions for the following
(a) Godfrey's age when Mary is $t$ years old.
(b) Mary's age when Godfrey is $x$ years old.

**2** A cup of coffee costs $x$ pence and a cup of tea costs $y$ pence.
Write an expression for the cost of 3 cups of coffee and 2 cups of tea.

**3** Simplify (a) $m + 2m + 3m$, (b) $2m + 2 - m$, (c) $m \times m \times m$.

**4** Write an expression, in terms of $x$,
for the sum of the angles in this shape.

**5** A muffin costs $d + 3$ pence.
Write an expression for the cost of 5 muffins.

**6** Which of these algebraic expressions are equivalent?

| $a + a$ | $2(a + 1)$ | $2a + 1$ | $2a + 2$ | $a^3$ |
|---------|------------|----------|----------|-------|
| $a^2$ | $a + a + 1$ | $2a$ | $a + a + a$ | $a \times a$ |

**7** (a) Simplify (i) $2x + 3 + x$, (ii) $2x + y - x + y$.
(b) Multiply out (i) $2(x + 3)$, (ii) $x(x - 1)$.
(c) Multiply out and simplify (i) $2(x - 1) - 3$, (ii) $7 + 3(2 + x)$.
(d) Factorise (i) $2a - 6$, (ii) $x^2 + 2x$.

**8** (a) Simplify $2ab + 3a - 2b + b - 5a + ab$.
(b) Multiply out and simplify $3(2x + 3) + 2(5 + x)$.

**9** Ahmed and Hussein are two brothers. Ahmed is older than Hussein.
Given that Ahmed's age is $(5x - 4)$ years and Hussein's age is $(2x + 1)$ years,
write down an expression, in terms of $x$, for how much older Ahmed is than Hussein.
Simplify your answer. Edexcel

**10** Lorna buys some 1st class stamps and some 2nd class stamps.
She buys 12 stamps altogether.
(a) She buys $x$ 1st class stamps.
Write an expression for the number of 2nd class stamps she buys.
(b) 2nd class stamps cost $d$ pence.
A 1st class stamp costs 5 pence more than a 2nd class stamp.
Write an expression for the cost of a 1st class stamp.
(c) Write an expression, in terms of $x$ and $d$, for the amount Lorna has to pay for her
12 stamps. Give your answer in its simplest form.

**11** Simplify. (a) $y^3 \times y^2$ (b) $x^6 \div x^3$ (c) $\dfrac{z^4 \times z}{z^3}$ (d) $\dfrac{x^2 y}{xy^2}$

**12** (a) Multiply out $t^2(t^3 - t^4)$.
(b) Multiply out and simplify $3(2a + 6) - 2(3a - 6)$.
(c) Simplify $\dfrac{12a^2 b}{4ab}$. Edexcel

**13** Factorise completely (a) $x^2 - 3x$, (b) $2p^2 q + pq^2$. Edexcel

**14** (a) Simplify $5 - 3(2n - 1)$.
(b) Multiply out $(-3m) \times (-2m)$.
(c) Factorise fully $8mn - 2m$.

**15** (a) Simplify (i) $2a^3 \times 3a$, (ii) $6x^8 \div 3x^2$, (iii) $\dfrac{3m^2 \times 4n^6}{6mn^2}$, (iv) $4x^3 y \times 5x^2 y$.
(b) Expand (i) $(3m^3)^2$, (ii) $(2a^2 b)^3$.

**16** (a) $x^2 \times x^3 = x^p$. Write down the value of $p$.
(b) $\sqrt{x} = x^q$. Write down the value of $q$.
(c) $(x^2 \times x^3) \div \sqrt{x} = x^r$. Find the value of $r$. Edexcel

**17** (a) Expand the brackets. (i) $2x(x - 3y)$ (ii) $3a(3a + a^2)$
(b) Factorise. (i) $4xy - 2y^2$ (ii) $3m^2 - 12m$
(c) Simplify. $2x^2 - x(1 + x)$

**18** Simplify fully. $5x^3 y^4 \times 7xy^2$ Edexcel

**19** (a) Multiply out $2x(2y - xy)$.
(b) Factorise $6pq - 3pq^2$.
(c) Simplify $21m^6 \div 7m^3$.

**20** Simplify. (a) $\dfrac{6x^2 z \times 2x^2 y^2 z}{3x^3 y}$ (b) $\sqrt{\dfrac{1}{m^6}}$ (c) $(4x^2 y)^3$

**21** Simplify fully $\dfrac{3a^2}{bc} \times \dfrac{b^2}{6ac^2} \times \dfrac{2ac^2}{b}$.

## What you need to know

- The solution of an equation is the value of the unknown letter that fits the equation.
- You should be able to solve simple equations by **inspection**.
- Be able to solve simple problems by **working backwards**.

  **Eg 1** I think of a number, multiply it by 3 and add 4. The answer is 19.

  The number I thought of is 5.

- Be able to use the **balance method** to solve equations.

  **Eg 2** Solve these equations.

  (a) $d - 13 = -5$

  $d = -5 + 13$

  $d = 8$

  (b) $-4a = 20$

  $a = \frac{20}{-4}$

  $a = -5$

  (c) $5 - 4n = -1$

  $-4n = -6$

  $n = 1.5$

- Be able to solve equations with unknowns on both sides of the equals sign.

  **Eg 3** Solve $3x + 1 = x + 7$.

  $3x = x + 6$

  $2x = 6$

  $x = 3$

- Be able to solve equations which include brackets.

  **Eg 4** Solve $4(3 + 2x) = 5(x + 2)$.

  $12 + 8x = 5x + 10$

  $8x = 5x - 2$

  $3x = -2$

  $x = -\frac{2}{3}$

- Be able to solve equations which involve fractions.

  **Eg 5** Solve $\frac{x}{2} + \frac{2x}{3} = 7$.

  $6 \times \frac{x}{2} + 6 \times \frac{2x}{3} = 6 \times 7$

  $3x + 4x = 42$

  $7x = 42$

  $x = 6$

  **Eg 6** Solve $\frac{x-1}{3} = \frac{x+1}{4}$.

  $4(x - 1) = 3(x + 1)$

  $4x - 4 = 3x + 3$

  $4x = 3x + 7$

  $x = 7$

- You should be able to write, or form, equations using the information given in a problem.

## Exercise **11**

**1** Solve these equations.    (a) $7 + x = 12$    (b) $5 - x = 3$    (c) $5x - 9 = 11$

**2** (a) I think of a number, add 3, and then multiply by 2. The answer is 16.
  What is my number?

  (b) I think of a number, double it and then subtract 3. The answer is 5.
  What is my number?

**3** Solve these equations.

  (a) $3x - 7 = 23$    (b) $5 + 7x = 47$    (c) $5(x - 2) = 20$    (d) $3x - 7 = x + 15$

**4** The lengths of these rods are given, in centimetres, in terms of $n$.

The total length of the rods is $30\,\text{cm}$.
By forming an equation, find the value of $n$.

**5** Solve these equations.
(a)   $3y + 7 = 28$   (b)   $2(3p + 2) = 19$   (c)   $3t - 4 = 5t - 10$   Edexcel

**6** Solve.
(a)   $4a + 3 = 9$   (b)   $5b - 7 = 2b + 5$   (c)   $3(c - 6) = 10 - 2c$   Edexcel

**7** Solve $2(5x + 3) = 3x - 22$.   Edexcel

**8**

The diagram shows two straight lines $AB$ and $CD$. Each line is cut into sections.
The length, in centimetres, of each section is shown in the diagram.
(a)   Write down, in terms of $d$,   (i)   the length of $AB$,   (ii)   the length of $CD$.

The length of $AB$ is equal to the length of $CD$.
(b)   (i)   Write down an equation in $d$.
      (ii)   Solve your equation to find the value of $d$.   Edexcel

**9** Solve these equations.
(a)   $\frac{x}{3} = -7$   (b)   $2(x - 1) = 3$   (c)   $5 - 2x = 3x + 2$   (d)   $\frac{1}{4}x + 5 = 2$

**10** Solve the equations   (a)   $5(2p - 3) = 50$,   (b)   $\frac{16 - q}{3} = 3$.   Edexcel

**11** Solve these equations.
(a)   $\frac{x + 5}{2} = 3$   (b)   $\frac{1 - 2x}{3} = 2$   (c)   $\frac{3}{2} = \frac{3x}{5}$   (d)   $\frac{x}{2} + \frac{x}{3} = 5$

**12** The areas of three tiles are shown.
The area of the small tile **plus** the area of the
medium tile is equal to half the area of the large tile.

| Small | Medium | Large |
|-------|--------|-------|
| $(x - 2)\,\text{cm}^2$ | $2x\,\text{cm}^2$ | $(5x + 9)\,\text{cm}^2$ |

By forming an equation in terms of $x$, find the area of the large tile.

**13** Solve.   (a)   $4 = \frac{22}{p}$   (b)   $7r + 2 = 5(r - 4)$   Edexcel

**14** Solve the equations   (a)   $\frac{x - 3}{4} = 1 - x$,   (b)   $\frac{x - 3}{2} = \frac{2x + 1}{3}$.

**15** Solve the equation $\frac{1}{2}(x - 3) = \frac{1}{4}(3x - 1)$.

**16** Solve.   $\frac{y + 1}{3} = \frac{1 - y}{2}$   Edexcel

**17** Solve the equation $\frac{x - 1}{3} + \frac{x + 1}{2} = \frac{5}{6}$.

**18** Solve the equation $\frac{2(x + 1)}{3} - \frac{x + 2}{5} = 4$.

# Formulae ●●●●●●●●●●●●●●●●

## What you need to know

- An **expression** is just an answer using letters and numbers.
  A **formula** is an algebraic rule. It always has an equals sign.

- You should be able to **write simple formulae**.

  **Eg 1** A packet of crisps weighs 25 grams.
  Write a formula for the total weight,
  $W$ grams, of $n$ packets of crisps.
  $$W = 25n$$

  **Eg 2** Start with $t$, add 5 and then multiply
  by 3. The result is $p$.
  Write a formula for $p$ in terms of $t$.
  $$p = 3(t + 5)$$

- Be able to **substitute** values into expressions and formulae.

  **Eg 3**
  (a) $A = pq - r$
  Find the value of $A$
  when $p = 2$,
  $q = -2$ and $r = 3$.

  $A = pq - r$
  $A = 2 \times (-2) - 3$
  $A = -4 - 3$
  $A = -7$

  (b) $M = 2n^2$
  Find the value of $M$
  when $n = 3$.

  $M = 2n^2$
  $M = 2 \times 3^2$
  $M = 2 \times 9$
  $M = 18$

  (c) Find the value of $\dfrac{b^2c}{d}$
  when $b = \frac{1}{2}$, $c = 4.8$
  and $d = -3$.

  $\dfrac{b^2c}{d} = \dfrac{\left(\frac{1}{2}\right)^2 \times 4.8}{-3}$

  $\dfrac{b^2c}{d} = \dfrac{\frac{1}{4} \times 4.8}{-3}$

  $\dfrac{b^2c}{d} = \dfrac{1.2}{-3}$

  $\dfrac{b^2c}{d} = 0.4$

- Be able to **rearrange** a formula to make another letter (variable) the subject.

  **Eg 4** $y = 2x + a$

  Make $x$ the subject of the formula.

  $y = 2x + a$
  $y - a = 2x$
  $\dfrac{y - a}{2} = x$
  So, $x = \dfrac{y - a}{2}$

  **Eg 5** $T = ab^2$
  Rearrange the formula to give $b$
  in terms of $T$ and $a$.

  $T = ab^2$
  $\dfrac{T}{a} = b^2$
  $b = \pm \sqrt{\dfrac{T}{a}}$

## Exercise 12

Do not use a calculator for questions 1 to 12.

**1** Given that $m = -3$ and $n = 5$, find the value of
(a) $m + n$, (b) $m - n$, (c) $n - m$, (d) $mn$.

**2** If $p = 4$ and $q = -5$ find the value of (a) $3pq$, (b) $p^2 + 2q$.

**3** $L = 5(p + q)$. Find the value of $L$ when $p = 2$ and $q = -0.4$.

**4** $A = b - cd$. Find the value of $A$ when $b = -3$, $c = 2$ and $d = 4$.

**5** What is the value of $10y^2$ when $y = 3$?

**6** What is the value of $3x^3$ when $x = 2$?

**7** $T = ab^2$. Find the value of $T$ when $a = 4$ and $b = -5$.

**8** $P = Q^2 - 2Q.$  Find the value of $P$ when $Q = -3$ Edexcel

**9** $T = \frac{uv}{w}.$  Find the value of $T$ when $u = 3,$ $v = -2$ and $w = \frac{1}{2}.$

**10** $M = \sqrt{\frac{a}{b}}.$  Find the value of $M$ when $a = 8$ and $b = \frac{1}{2}.$

**11** A pen costs 25 pence. A pencil costs 10 pence.
Louisa buys $x$ pens and $y$ pencils.
The total cost is $C$ pence.
(a) Write a formula for $C$ in terms of $x$ and $y$.
(b) Work out the value of $y$ when $C = 250$ and $x = 6.$ Edexcel

**12** $c = y - mx.$  Calculate the value of $c$ when $y = 4.95,$ $m = -0.75$ and $x = 3.$ Edexcel

**13** A formula is given as $c = 3t - 5.$
Rearrange the formula to give $t$ in terms of $c$.

**14** $s = \frac{1}{2}(u + v)t.$  Work out the value of $s$ when $u = 10,$ $v = -25$ and $t = 0.5.$ Edexcel

**15** Rearrange the formula $n = 3 + mp$ to make $m$ the subject.

**16** The diagram shows a solid.
The volume, $V$, of the solid is given by the formula
$$V = \frac{\pi h}{3}(R^2 + Rr + r^2)$$
(a) $h = 6.8,$ $R = 9.7$ and $r = 5.3.$
Calculate the value of $V$.
Give your answer correct to 3 significant figures.
(b) Make $h$ the subject of the formula.
(c) $V = 200,$ $h = 10$ and $R = 2r.$
Calculate the value of $R$.
Give your answer correct to 3 significant figures. Edexcel

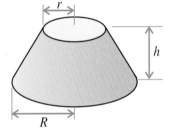

**17** $m = \frac{3}{5}(n - 17).$  Find the value of $n$ when $m = -9.$

**18** Make $a$ the subject of the formula $2(3a - c) = 5c + 1.$ Edexcel

**19** You are given the formula $v = u + at.$
(a) Find $v$ when $u = 17,$ $a = -8$ and $t = \frac{3}{5}.$
(b) Rearrange the formula to give $a$ in terms of $v$, $u$ and $t$.

**20** Make $s$ the subject of the formula $t = s^2 + 5.$

**21** Make $x$ the subject of the formula $y = \frac{x^2 + 4}{5}.$ Edexcel

**22** $v^2 = u^2 + 2as.$  Calculate the value of $v$, when $u = 8,$ $a = -3$ and $s = 5.5.$ Edexcel

**23** You are given the formula $g = \frac{3}{5}h^2.$
(a) Find the value of $g$ when $h = 2.5 \times 10^3.$
(b) Rearrange the formula to give $h$ in terms of $g$.

**24** Rearrange the formula $p = \frac{q}{5 - q}$ to make $q$ the subject.

**25** Make $v$ the subject of the formula $w = \frac{uv}{u + v}.$

**26** $n = \frac{3 + m}{m - 5}.$  Rearrange the formula to give $m$ in terms of $n$.

**27** Rearrange $4y = k(2 - 3y)$ to write $y$ in terms of $k$. Edexcel

## What you need to know

- A **sequence** is a list of numbers made according to some rule.
  The numbers in a sequence are called **terms**.

- You should be able to draw and continue number sequences represented by patterns of shapes.

- Be able to continue a sequence by following a given rule.

  **Eg 1** The sequence 2, 7, 22, … is made using the rule:

  > Multiply the last number by 3, then add 1.

  The next term in the sequence $= (22 \times 3) + 1 = 66 + 1 = 67$

- Be able to find a rule, and then use it, to continue a sequence. .

  > **To continue a sequence:**
  > 1. Work out the rule to get from one term to the next.
  > 2. Apply the same rule to find further terms in the sequence.

  **Eg 2** Describe the rule used to make the following sequences.
  Then use the rule to find the next term of each sequence.
  (a) 5, 8, 11, 14, …     Rule: add 3 to last term.     Next term: 17.
  (b) 2, 4, 8, 16, …     Rule: multiply last term by 2.   Next term: 32.
  (c) 1, 1, 2, 3, 5, 8, …    Rule: add the last two terms.   Next term: 13.

- Special sequences   **Square numbers:**    1, 4, 9, 16, 25, …
                      **Triangular numbers:** 1, 3, 6, 10, 15, …

- A number sequence which increases (or decreases) by the same amount from one term to the next is called a **linear sequence**.
  The sequence: 2, 8, 14, 20, 26, … has a **common difference** of 6.

- You should be able to find an expression for the $n$th term of a linear sequence.

  **Eg 3** Find the $n$th term of the sequence: 3, 5, 7, 9, …
  The sequence is linear, common difference $= 2$.
  To find the $n$th term add one to the multiples of 2.
  So, the $n$th term is $2n + 1$.

- Be able to find an expression for the $n$th term of a **quadratic sequence**.

  **Eg 4** Find the $n$th term of the sequence: 4, 7, 12, 19, …
  The sequence is not linear, because the differences between terms is increasing.
  Compare the sequence with the sequence of square numbers: 1, 4, 9, 16, …
  To find the $n$th term add 3 to the square numbers.
  So, the $n$th term is $n^2 + 3$.

## Exercise 13

**1** What is the next number in each of these sequences?

(a) 1, 2, 5, 10, …       (b) 1, 3, 9, 27, …       (c) 1, $\frac{1}{2}$, $\frac{1}{4}$, $\frac{1}{8}$, …

**2** Here are the first five terms of a number sequence.

$$3 \quad 8 \quad 13 \quad 18 \quad 23$$

(a) Write down the next **two** terms of the sequence.
(b) Explain how you found your answer.
(c) Explain why 387 is **not** a term of the sequence.
Edexcel

**3** Here are the first four terms in a sequence: 6, 12, 18, 24.

(a) (i) Write down the 5th term in the sequence.
  (ii) Explain how you worked out your answer.
(b) Which term in the sequence is equal to 72?
Edexcel

**4** (a) The rule for a sequence of numbers is:

> ADD THE TWO PREVIOUS NUMBERS AND THEN MULTIPLY BY 2

Write down the next two numbers in the sequence: 1, 1, 4, 10, …

(b) The first eight numbers in a different sequence of numbers are:

$$3, \ 7, \ 4, \ 8, \ 5, \ 9, \ 6, \ 10, \ \dots$$

Write down the next two numbers in the sequence.
Edexcel

**5** The first six terms of a sequence are shown. 1, 4, 5, 9, 14, 23, …
Write down the next two terms.

**6** A sequence begins: 1, 6, 10, 8, … The rule to continue the sequence is:
**double the difference between the last two numbers**.
Ravi says if you continue the sequence it will end in 0. Is he correct? Explain your answer.

**7** The first three patterns in a sequence are shown.

Pattern 1      Pattern 2      Pattern 3

(a) How many squares are in pattern 20? Explain how you found your answer.
(b) Write an expression for the number of squares in the $n$th pattern.

**8** Here are the first four terms of a number sequence: 3, 7, 11, 15.
(a) Write down the next two terms of the sequence.
(b) Write down an expression, in terms of $n$, for the $n$th term of the sequence.
Edexcel

**9** Find the $n$th term of the following sequences.
(a) 5, 7, 9, 11, …    (b) 1, 5, 9, 13, …    (c) $-2, \ -1, \ 0, \ 1, \ \dots$

**10** Marco writes down a number sequence. He starts at 120.
Each time he subtracts 12 to get the next number in the sequence.
(a) Write down the first 5 numbers in the sequence.
(b) Write down an expression for the $n$th number in the sequence.
Edexcel

**11** (a) Write down the first **three** terms of the sequence whose $n$th term is given by $n^2 - 4$.
(b) Will the number 60 be in this sequence? Explain your answer.

**12** A sequence begins: 3, 6, 11, 18, 27, …
(a) Find the next two terms in this sequence.
(b) Explain why this is not a linear sequence.
(c) Explain how you can find the 20th term in the sequence without writing down all the previous terms.

**13** Give the $n$th term of the following sequences.
(a) 1, 4, 9, 16, 25, 36, …
(b) 4, 7, 12, 19, 28, 39, …

# Straight Line Graphs ●●●●●●●

## What you need to know

- **Coordinates** are used to describe the position of a point on a graph.

- The $x$ axis is the line $y = 0$.
  The $y$ axis is the line $x = 0$.

- The graph of a linear function is a straight line.

- You should be able to draw the graph of a straight line.

  **Eg 1** Draw the graph of $y = x + 1$ for values of $x$ from $-2$ to 2.

  > To draw a linear graph:
  > Find two corresponding values of $x$ and $y$.
  > Plot the points.
  > Join the points with a straight line.

  When $x = -2$, $y = -2 + 1 = -1$. Plot $(-2, -1)$.
  When $x = 2$, $y = 2 + 1 = 3$. Plot $(2, 3)$.
  A straight line drawn through the points $(-2, -1)$ and $(2, 3)$ is the graph of $y = x + 1$.

- The equation of the graph of a straight line is of the form $y = mx + c$,
  where $m$ is the gradient and $c$ is the $y$-intercept.

  The **gradient** of a line can be found by drawing a
  right-angled triangle.

  $$\text{Gradient} = \frac{\text{distance up}}{\text{distance along}}$$

  Gradients can be positive, zero or negative.

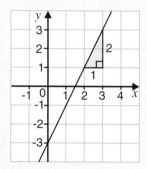

  **Eg 2** Find the equation of the line shown on this graph.

  Gradient of line $= \dfrac{\text{distance up}}{\text{distance along}} = \dfrac{2}{1} = 2$

  The graph crosses the $y$ axis at the point $(0, -3)$,
  so, the $y$-intercept is $-3$.
  The equation of the line is $y = 2x - 3$.

- The points where a line crosses the axes can be found:
  by reading the coordinates from a graph,
  by substituting $x = 0$ and $y = 0$ into the equation of the line.

  **Eg 3** The diagram shows a sketch of the line $2y = x + 3$.

  Find the coordinates of the points $P$ and $Q$.

  When $x = 0$, $2y = 0 + 3$, $2y = 3$, $y = 1\frac{1}{2}$.

  When $y = 0$, $0 = x + 3$, $x = -3$.

  The points are $P\left(0, 1\frac{1}{2}\right)$ and $Q(-3, 0)$.

● You should be able to find the gradient of a line which is perpendicular to a given line.

> If two lines are perpendicular to each other, the product of their gradients $= -1$.
>
> This can be written as: $m_{AB} \times m_{CD} = -1$
>
> where $m_{AB}$ is the gradient of the line $AB$,
> and $m_{CD}$ is the gradient of the line $CD$.

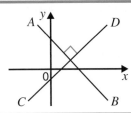

$$m_{AB} = \frac{-1}{m_{CD}}$$

**Eg 4** Write down the gradient of the line which is perpendicular to the line with equation $y = -3x + 4$.
The gradient of the line $y = -3x + 4$ is $-3$.
The gradient of the line which is perpendicular to this line is $-1 \div (-3) = \frac{1}{3}$.

● Equations of the form $px + qy = r$ can be **rearranged** to the form $y = mx + c$.

**Eg 5** The graph of a straight line is given by the equation $4y - 3x = 8$.
Write this equation in the form $y = mx + c$.

$4y - 3x = 8$
$4y = 3x + 8$
$y = \frac{3}{4}x + 2$

| The line has gradient $\frac{3}{4}$ and $y$-intercept 2. |

● You should be able to solve equations and problems involving straight line graphs.

## Exercise 14

**1** (a) Copy and complete this table of values for $y = 2x + 3$.

| $x$ | $-3$ | $-2$ | $-1$ | 0 | 1 | 2 |
|-----|------|------|------|---|---|---|
| $y$ |      | $-1$ |      |   |   |   |

(b) Draw the graph of $y = 2x + 3$ for values of $x$ from $-3$ to 2.
(c) Use your graph to find  (i) the value of $y$ when $x = 1.5$,
  (ii) the value of $x$ when $y = -0.5$.  *Edexcel*

**2** (a) On the same axes, draw the graphs of $y = -2$, $y = x$ and $x + y = 5$.
(b) Which of these lines has a negative gradient?

**3**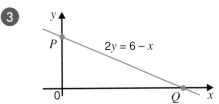
The diagram shows a sketch of the line $2y = 6 - x$.
(a) Find the coordinates of the points $P$ and $Q$.
(b) The line $2y = 6 - x$ goes through $R(-5, m)$.
What is the value of $m$?

**4** Points $P$, $Q$ and $R$ are shown on the grid.
(a) Write down the equation of the line $PQ$.
(b) (i) Use the grid to work out the gradient of the line $RP$.
  (ii) Write down the equation of the line $RP$.

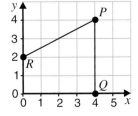

**5** Match these equations to their graphs.

**1**   $y = 2x$

**2**   $y - x = 2$

**3**   $y + x = 2$

**4**   $2y = x$

P

Q

R

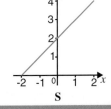

S

**6** (a) Draw the graph of $2y = 3x - 6$ for values of $x$ from $-2$ to 4.

(b) What is the gradient of the line $2y = 3x - 6$?

(c) Use your graph to find the value of $x$ when $y = 1.5$.

**7** A straight line, $L$, has been drawn on the grid.

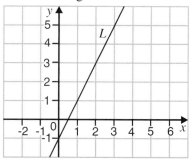

(a) Find an equation of the line $L$.

(b) Find an equation of the line through $(1, 2)$ parallel to $L$.

Edexcel

**8** Errol's house has a meter which measures the amount of water he uses. The graph can be used to find out how much he must pay for the number of water units that he uses.

Cost in £

Number of units

Errol uses $x$ water units. This costs £$c$.

Use the information from the graph to find a formula for $c$ in terms of $x$.

Edexcel

**9** The equation of a line is $5y - 2x = 10$.

(a) Write this equation in the form $y = mx + c$.

(b) Write down the equation of the line, parallel to $5y - 2x = 10$, which passes through the point $(0, -1)$.

**10** Show that the lines $5y = x + 4$ and $y = 6 - 5x$ are perpendicular to each other.

**11** The diagram shows the graph of $2y = x + 4$.

Find the equation of the line through $B$ which is perpendicular to the line $2y = x + 4$.

## What you need to know

● A **gradient** measures the **rate of change** of one quantity with respect to another.
A **positive** gradient represents a **rate of increase**.
A **negative** gradient represents a **rate of decrease**.

● The gradient of a **distance-time graph** gives the speed.

> **Speed** is the rate of change of distance with respect to time.
> When the distance-time graph is **linear** the **speed is constant**.
> When the distance-time graph is **horizontal** the **speed is zero**.

**Eg 1** The graph shows a car journey.
  (a) Between what times does the car travel fastest?
      Explain your answer.
  (b) What is the speed of the car during this part
      of the journey?

  (a) 1200 to 1230. Steepest gradient.

  (b) Speed $= \dfrac{\text{Distance}}{\text{Time}} = \dfrac{20\,\text{km}}{\frac{1}{2}\,\text{hour}} = 40\,\text{km/h}$

● The gradient of a **speed-time graph** gives the acceleration.

> **Acceleration** is the rate of change of speed with respect to time.
> When the speed-time graph is **linear** the **acceleration is constant**.
> When the speed-time graph is **horizontal** the **speed is constant** and the **acceleration is zero**.

● The **area** enclosed by the graph on a speed-time graph represents the **distance** travelled.

**Eg 2** The graph shows the speed of a car against time between two roundabouts.
  (a) Calculate the acceleration of the car.
  (b) Calculate the distance travelled.

  (a) Acceleration $= \dfrac{\text{Speed}}{\text{Time}} = \dfrac{10\,\text{m/s}}{15\,\text{s}} = 0.67\,\text{m/s}^2$

  (b) Distance travelled $= \frac{1}{2}(15 + 35) \times 10 = 250$ metres

● You should be able to draw and interpret graphs which represent real-life situations.

## Exercise 15

**1** Water is poured into some containers at a constant rate.
Copy the axes given and sketch the graph of the depth of the water against time for each
container as it is filled.

(a)

(b)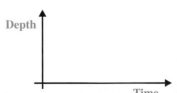

**②** Ken and Wendy go from home to their caravan site.
The caravan site is 50 km from their home.
Ken goes on his bike. Wendy drives in her car.
The diagram shows information about the journeys they made.

(a)  At what time did Wendy pass Ken?
(b)  Between which two times was Ken cycling at his greatest speed?
(c)  Work out Wendy's average speed for her journey.                    Edexcel

**③** Here is part of a travel graph of Siân's journey from her house to the shops and back.

(a)  Work out Siân's speed for the first 30 minutes of her journey.
     Give your answer in km/h.

Siân spends 15 minutes at the shops.
She then travels back to her house at 60 km/h.
(b)  Copy and complete the travel graph.                    Edexcel

**④** The speed-time graph of a vehicle during the final minute of a journey is shown.

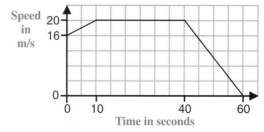

(a)  Calculate the acceleration of the vehicle in the first 10 seconds.
(b)  Calculate the total distance travelled by the vehicle in this minute.    Edexcel

# Inequalities ●●●●●●●●●●●●●

## What you need to know

● **Inequalities** can be described using words or numbers and symbols.

| Sign | Meaning |
|------|---------|
| $<$ | is less than |
| $\leqslant$ | is less than or equal to |

| Sign | Meaning |
|------|---------|
| $>$ | is greater than |
| $\geqslant$ | is greater than or equal to |

● Inequalities can be shown on a **number line**.

**Eg 1** This diagram shows the inequality: $-2 < x \leqslant 3$

```
  ○——————————————●
-3  -2  -1   0   1   2   3   4
```

The circle is: **filled** if the inequality is **included** (i.e. $\leqslant$ or $\geqslant$),
**not filled** if the inequality is **not included** (i.e. $<$ or $>$).

● **Solving inequalities** means finding the values of $x$ which make the inequality true.

The same rules for equations can be applied to inequalities, with one exception:
When you **multiply** (or **divide**) both sides of an inequality by a negative number
the inequality is reversed. For example, if $-3x < 6$ then $x > -2$.

**Eg 2** Solve these inequalities.

(a) $7a \geqslant a + 9$
$6a \geqslant 9$
$a \geqslant 1.5$

(b) $-3x < 6$
$x > -2$

Divide both sides by $-3$.
Because we are dividing by a negative
number the inequality is reversed.

**Eg 3** Find the integer values of $n$ for which $-1 \leqslant 2n + 3 < 7$.
$-1 \leqslant 2n + 3 < 7$
$-4 \leqslant 2n < 4$
$-2 \leqslant n < 2$

Integer values which satisfy the inequality $-1 \leqslant 2n + 3 < 7$ are: $-2, -1, 0, 1$

● Inequalities can be shown on a graph. A line divides the graph into two **regions**.

**To show an inequality on a graph:** Replace the inequality by '$=$' and draw the line.
For $>$ and $<$ the line is **broken**. For $\geqslant$ and $\leqslant$ the line is **solid**.
Test a point on each side of the line to see whether its coordinates satisfy the inequality.
Label the required region.

**Eg 4** Show the region which satisfies
these inequalities:
$y < 3$, $1 < x < 4$ and $2y > x$.

**Eg 5** Use inequalities to describe the
shaded region in this diagram.

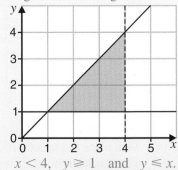

$x < 4$, $y \geqslant 1$ and $y \leqslant x$.

**1** Solve these inequalities.

(a) $5x > 15$ (b) $x + 3 \geqslant 1$ (c) $x - 5 \leqslant 1$ (d) $3 + 2x > 7$

**2** Draw number lines to show each of these inequalities.

(a) $x \geqslant -2$ (b) $\frac{x}{3} < -1$ (c) $-1 < x \leqslant 3$ (d) $x \leqslant -1$ **and** $x > 3$

**3** List all the possible integer values of $n$ such that $-3 \leqslant n < 2$. Edexcel

**4** $n$ is a whole number such that $6 < 2n < 13$. List all the possible values of $n$. Edexcel

**5** List the values of $n$, where $n$ is an integer such that:

(a) $-2 \leqslant 2n < 6$ (b) $-3 < n - 3 \leqslant -1$ (c) $-5 \leqslant 2n - 3 < 1$

**6** Solve the inequalities. (a) $2x - 5 > x + 2$ (b) $-9 < 5x + 1 \leqslant 6$

**7** Solve the inequality $7y > 2y - 3$. Edexcel

**8** Match each of the inequalities to its **unshaded** region.

**1** $x + y < 2$

**2** $y > 2$

**3** $y > x$

**4** $x < 2$

 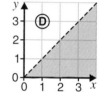

**9** Draw and label axes for both $x$ and $y$ from 0 to 4.

(a) On your diagram draw and label the lines $y = 1$ and $x + y = 3$.

(b) Show clearly on the diagram the single region that is satisfied by all of these inequalities.
$x \geqslant 0$, $y \geqslant 1$, $x + y \leqslant 3$. Label this region $R$.

**10** Write down three inequalities which describe the shaded region.

**11** (a) Draw and label axes for $x$ from $-1$ to 4 and for $y$ from 0 to 6.
On your diagram draw and label the following lines.
$y = 5$, $y = x + 1$ and $y = 6 - 2x$.

(b) Show clearly the single region that is satisfied by **all** of these inequalities.
$x \geqslant 0$, $y \leqslant 5$, $y \geqslant x + 1$, $y \leqslant 6 - 2x$.

**12** (a) Solve the inequality $5x - 7 < 2x - 1$.

(b) Represent the solution set to part (a) on a number line. Edexcel

**13** (a) Solve the inequality $-4 \leqslant 2(x + 3) < 8$.

(b) $n$ is an integer.
Find the maximum value of $n$ that satisfies the inequality $-4 \leqslant 2(x + 3) < 8$.

**14** (a) Solve each of the following inequalities. (i) $2x - 7 \leqslant 8 - x$ (ii) $3(2x + 1) > 15$

(b) Write down the whole number values of $x$ which satisfy both of the above inequalities simultaneously.

SECTION **17** **Further Graphs** •••••••••

## What you need to know

- The graph of a **quadratic function** is a smooth curve and is called a **parabola**.

- The general equation of a **quadratic function** is $y = ax^2 + bx + c$, where $a$ cannot be zero. The graph of a quadratic function is symmetrical and has a **maximum** or **minimum** value.

- You should be able to plot graphs of quadratic functions and use the graphs of quadratic functions to solve **quadratic equations**.

  **Eg 1** (a) Draw the graph of $y = x^2 - x - 1$ for $-2 \leqslant x \leqslant 2$.
  (b) Hence, find the solutions of $x^2 - x - 1 = 0$.

  (a)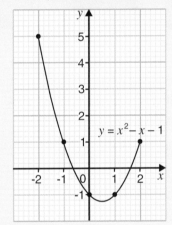

  To draw a quadratic graph:
  Make a table of values connecting $x$ and $y$.
  Plot the points.
  Join the points with a smooth curve.

  | $x$ | $-2$ | $-1$ | $0$ | $1$ | $2$ |
  |---|---|---|---|---|---|
  | $y$ | $5$ | $1$ | $-1$ | $-1$ | $1$ |

  (b) To solve $x^2 - x - 1 = 0$, read the values of $x$ where the graph of $y = x^2 - x - 1$ crosses the $x$ axis ($y = 0$).

  $x = -0.6$ and $x = 1.6$, correct to 1 d.p.

- Be able to use graphs of linear and quadratic functions to solve equations.

  **Eg 2** You are given the graph of $y = 2x - x^2$.
  By drawing a suitable linear graph, on the same axes, find the solutions of $x^2 - 3x + 1 = 0$.
  To find the linear graph:
  Rearrange $x^2 - 3x + 1 = 0$ to give $1 - x = 2x - x^2$.
  Hence, the linear graph is $y = 1 - x$.
  Draw the graph of $y = 1 - x$ on the same diagram.

  To solve $x^2 - 3x + 1 = 0$, read the values of $x$ where the two graphs intersect.

  So, $x = 0.4$ and $x = 2.6$, correct to 1 d.p.

- The general form of a **cubic function** is $y = ax^3 + bx^2 + cx + d$, where $a$ cannot be zero.

- The graph of the **reciprocal function** is of the form $y = \dfrac{a}{x}$, where $x$ cannot be equal to zero.

- The graph of the **exponential function** is of the form $y = a^x$.

- The graph of a **circle**, centre $(0, 0)$, is of the form $x^2 + y^2 = r^2$, where $r$ is the radius of the circle.

- You should be able to identify and sketch the graphs of functions. For example:

$y = x^3$     $y = \frac{1}{x}$     $y = 2^x$     $x^2 + y^2 = 16$

## Exercise 17

**1**   (a)   Copy and complete this table of values for $y = x^2 - 2$.

| $x$ | $-3$ | $-2$ | $-1$ | $0$ | $1$ | $2$ | $3$ |
|---|---|---|---|---|---|---|---|
| $y$ | | $2$ | | $-2$ | $-1$ | | $7$ |

   (b)   Draw the graph of $y = x^2 - 2$ for values of $x$ from $-3$ to $3$.
   (c)   Write down the values of $x$ at the points where the line $y = 3$ crosses your graph.
   (d)   Use your graph to solve the equation $x^2 - 2 = 0$.

**2**   (a)   Copy and complete this table of values for $y = x + \frac{1}{x}$.

| $x$ | $0.2$ | $0.4$ | $0.6$ | $0.8$ | $1$ | $2$ | $4$ | $5$ |
|---|---|---|---|---|---|---|---|---|
| $y$ | $5.2$ | | | | $2$ | | $4.25$ | $5.2$ |

   (b)   Use your table of values to draw the graph of $y = x + \frac{1}{x}$.
   (c)   Use your graph to find estimates for the solutions of the equation $x + \frac{1}{x} = 5$.    *Edexcel*

**3**   (a)   Draw the graph of $y = 5x - x^2$ for $-1 \leqslant x \leqslant 6$.
   (b)   Use your graph to solve the equation   (i)   $5x - x^2 = 0$,     (ii)   $5x - x^2 = 3$.

**4**   (a)   Draw the graph of $y = 2x^2 - 3x + 2$ for values of $x$ from $-2$ to $3$.
   (b)   Explain how the graph shows that there are no values of $x$ for which $2x^2 - 3x + 2 = 0$.
   (c)   State the minimum value of $y$.

**5**   (a)   Copy and complete the table of values for the graph of $y = 4x(11 - 2x)$.

| $x$ | $0$ | $1$ | $2$ | $3$ | $4$ | $5$ | $6$ |
|---|---|---|---|---|---|---|---|
| $y$ | $0$ | | | $60$ | | | $-24$ |

   (b)   Draw the graph of $y = 4x(11 - 2x)$.
   (c)   Use your graph to find the maximum value of $y$.    *Edexcel*

**6**   (a)   Using the same axes, draw the graphs with equations $y = 3x$ and $y = x^2 + 1$.
   (b)   Explain how you can use these graphs to solve the equation $x^2 - 3x + 1 = 0$.
   (c)   Hence, solve the equation $x^2 - 3x + 1 = 0$.

**7**   (a)   Draw the graph of $y = x^3 - x$ for $-3 \leqslant x \leqslant 3$.
   (b)   Use your graph to find the value of $x$ when $y = 10$.

**8**   On separate diagrams, sketch the graphs of these equations.
   Label any point where the graphs cross the $x$ or $y$ axes.
   (a)   $y = -x^3$      (b)   $xy = 4$      (c)   $x^2 + y^2 = 9$

**9**   (a)   Draw the graph of $y = 4^x$ for values of $x$ from $-2$ to $2$.
   (b)   Use your graph to find the value of $x$ when $y = 8$.

**10**   Find graphically the points of intersection of $x^2 + y^2 = 16$ and $2y = x - 1$.

Further Graphs ... Further Graphs ...

# Direct and Inverse Proportion

## What you need to know

- **Direct proportion**

  If $x$ and $y$ are quantities such that $y : x^n$ is always constant, then $y$ varies **directly** with $x^n$.

  This can be expressed:
  - in **words**: $y$ is **proportional** to $x^n$,
  - in **symbols**: $y \propto x^n$ (where $\propto$ means "is proportional to"),
  - as an **equation**: $y = kx^n$ (where $k$ is the **constant of proportionality**).

**Eg 1**  The cost, £$C$, of tiling a floor is proportional to the area of the floor, $a$ m$^2$.

It costs £60 to tile a floor of area 2 m$^2$.

(a) Find the formula connecting $C$ and $a$.

(b) A floor costs £150 to be tiled. What is the area of the floor?

(a)  $C = ka$
When  $C = 60$,  $a = 2$.
$60 = 2 \times k$
$k = 30$
$C = 30a$

(b)  $C = 30a$
When  $C = 150$.
$150 = 30a$
$a = 5$
Area of floor $= 5$ m$^2$

> Constant of proportionality, $k$. This can be calculated when corresponding values of $C$ and $a$ are known.

- **Inverse proportion**

  If $x$ and $y$ are quantities such that $y : \dfrac{1}{x^n}$ is always constant, then $y$ varies **inversely** with $x^n$.

  This can be expressed:
  - in **words**: $y$ is **inversely proportional** to $x^n$,
  - in **symbols**: $y \propto \dfrac{1}{x^n}$,
  - as an **equation**: $y = \dfrac{k}{x^n}$  or  $x^n y = k$.

**Eg 2**  $y$ is inversely proportional to $x^2$.  When  $x = 3$,  $y = 4$.

(a) Find the equation connecting $y$ and $x$.

(b) Find the value of $y$  when  $x = 2.4$.

(a)  $y = \dfrac{k}{x^2}$
When  $x = 3$,  $y = 4$.
$4 = \dfrac{k}{3^2}$,  so,  $k = 36$
$y = \dfrac{36}{x^2}$

(b)  $y = \dfrac{36}{x^2}$
When  $x = 2.4$.
$y = \dfrac{36}{(2.4)^2}$
$y = 6.25$

- The general form of a proportional relationship is  $y \propto x^n$  or  $y = kx^n$.

**Direct proportion,  $y = kx^n$,  $n > 0$**

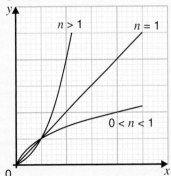

When:
  $n = 1$: $y$ increases at a constant rate.
  $0 < n < 1$: $y$ increases at a rate that decreases.
  $n > 1$: $y$ increases at a rate that increases.

**Inverse proportion,  $y = kx^n$,  $n < 0$**

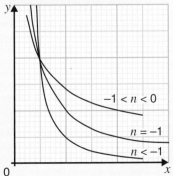

When:
  $n = -1$: the graph is symmetrical about the line $y = x$.

**1** The table shows values of $m$ and $n$.

| $m$ | 0.6 | 9 | 16.5 |
|---|---|---|---|
| $n$ | 0.4 | 6 | 11 |

(a) Show that $m$ is directly proportional to $n$.

(b) Find the value of (i) $m$ when $n = 1.8$,

(ii) $n$ when $m = 12.6$.

**2** The distance ($d$ metres) travelled by a stone falling vertically varies in direct proportion to the square of the time ($t$ seconds) for which it falls.

(a) Write a formula to connect $d$, $t$ and the constant of variation $k$.

A stone takes 2 seconds to fall 20 metres.

(b) Find the value of $k$.

(c) How far will the stone fall in 4 seconds?

A stone is dropped from a balloon which is 500 metres above the ground.

(d) How many seconds will the stone take to reach the ground? *Edexcel*

**3** $y$ is proportional to $x^3$. When $x = 3$, $y = 54$.

Find the value of $x$ when $y = 250$.

**4** $F$ varies inversely as the square of $d$. $F = 50$ when $d = 10$.

(a) Express $F$ in terms of $d$.

(b) (i) Calculate the value of $F$ when $d = 1000$.

(ii) Calculate the value of $d$ when $F = 500$. *Edexcel*

**5** $m$ is proportional to the square root of $n$. $m = 6$ when $n = 81$.

(a) Find the equation connecting $m$ and $n$.

(b) Calculate (i) the value of $m$ when $n = 36$,

(ii) the value of $n$ when $m = 10$.

**6** An artist hand-paints circular plates of different sizes.

The price, £$C$, of a hand-painted plate is proportional to the square of the radius, $r$ cm, of the plate.

The price of a plate of radius 6 cm is £9.

Calculate the price of a plate of radius 8 cm.

**7** $y$ is directly proportional to the cube of $x$. When $x = 2$, $y = 64$.

(a) Find an expression for $y$ in terms of $x$.

(b) Hence, or otherwise,

(i) calculate the value of $y$ when $x = \frac{1}{2}$,

(ii) calculate the value of $x$ when $y = 27$. *Edexcel*

**8** $y$ is proportional to $x^n$.

Sketch a graph of $y$ against $x$ when $x \geqslant 0$ and (a) $n = 2$, (b) $n = -2$.

**9** You are given that $y = 6x^n$ and that $y = 3$ when $x = 8$.

Find the value of $n$.

**10** $y$ is directly proportional to $x^2$. When $x = 2$, $y = 36$.

(a) Express $y$ in terms of $x$.

$z$ is inversely proportional to $x$. When $x = 3$, $z = 2$.

(b) Show that $z = cy^n$, where $c$ and $n$ are numbers and $c > 0$.

(You must find the values of $c$ and $n$). *Edexcel*

# Quadratic Equations

## What you need to know

- Brackets, such as $(x + 2)(x + 3)$, can be multiplied out using the **diagram method**, or by **expanding**.

**Eg 1** Multiply out $(x + 2)(x + 3)$.

$(x + 2)(x + 3) = x^2 + 3x + 2x + 6$
$= x^2 + 5x + 6$

**Eg 2** Expand $(x - 3)(2x + 1)$.

| | |
|---|---|
| **1** | $x \times 2x = 2x^2$ |
| **2** | $x \times 1 = x$ |
| **3** | $-3 \times 2x = -6x$ |
| **4** | $-3 \times 1 = -3$ |

$(x - 3)(2x + 1) = 2x^2 + x - 6x - 3$
$= 2x^2 - 5x - 3$

- **Factorising** is the opposite operation to removing brackets.

**Eg 3** Factorise the following.

(a) $x^2 + 3x = x(x + 3)$

(b) $2x^2 - 8 = 2(x^2 - 4)$
$= 2(x - 2)(x + 2)$

(c) $x^2 + 2x - 15 = (x + 5)(x - 3)$

> When factorising, work logically.
> 1. Does the expression have a **common factor**?
> 2. Is the expression a **difference of two squares**?
> $a^2 - b^2 = (a - b)(a + b)$
> 3. Will the expression factorise into **two brackets**?

- Some **quadratic equations** can be solved by factorising.

**Eg 4** Solve these equations.

(a) $x^2 - 5x = 0$
$x(x - 5) = 0$
$x = 0$ or $x = 5$

(b) $m^2 + m - 6 = 0$
$(m - 2)(m + 3) = 0$
$m = 2$ or $m = -3$

(c) $2a^2 - 5a - 3 = 0$
$(2a + 1)(a - 3) = 0$
$a = -\frac{1}{2}$ or $a = 3$

- The general form for a **quadratic equation** is $ax^2 + bx + c = 0$ where $a$ cannot be zero.

- The solutions to a quadratic equation can be found using the **quadratic formula**.

> If $ax^2 + bx + c = 0$ and $a \neq 0$ then $x = \dfrac{-b \pm \sqrt{b^2 - 4ac}}{2a}$

**Eg 5** Solve $x^2 - 3x - 2 = 0$.

$x = \dfrac{-(-3) \pm \sqrt{(-3)^2 - 4(1)(-2)}}{2(1)}$

$x = \dfrac{3 \pm \sqrt{17}}{2}$

$x = -0.56$ or $x = 3.56$, correct to two decimal places.

> Substitute: $a = 1$, $b = -3$ and $c = -2$,
> into $x = \dfrac{-b \pm \sqrt{b^2 - 4ac}}{2a}$

- Quadratic expressions, such as $x^2 + 8x + 20$, can be written in the form $(x + a)^2 + b$, where $a$ and $b$ are integers.

> In **completed square form**, $(x + a)^2 + b$:
> the value of $a$ is half the coefficient of $x$, the value of $b$ is found by subtracting the value of $a^2$ from the constant term of the original expression.

**Eg 6** $x^2 + 8x + 20 = (x + a)^2 + b$
$a = \frac{1}{2}(8) = 4$
$b = 20 - 4^2 = 4$
$x^2 + 8x + 20 = (x + 4)^2 + 4$

- Quadratic equations can be solved by **completing the square**.

**Eg 7** Solve $x^2 + 4x = 5$.

$$(x + 2)^2 - 4 = 5$$
$$(x + 2)^2 = 9$$
$$x + 2 = \pm 3$$
$$x + 2 = 3 \quad \text{or} \quad x + 2 = -3$$
$$x = 1 \quad \text{or} \quad x = -5$$

> Write the left-hand side (LHS) of the equation in the form $(x + a)^2 + b$ by completing the square.
> $$x^2 + 4x = (x + 2)^2 - 4$$

- You should be able to form and solve quadratic equations.

## Exercise 19

**1** Multiply out and simplify. (a) $x(x - 7)$ (b) $(x - 2)(x + 5)$

**2** In the diagram each side of the square $ABCD$ is $(3 + x)$ cm.
(a) Write down an expression in terms of $x$ for the area, in cm², of the square $ABCD$.

The actual area of the square $ABCD$ is $10$ cm².
(b) Show that $x^2 + 6x = 1$.

Edexcel

**3** Factorise. (a) $x^2 - 6x$ (b) $x^2 + 2x - 15$

**4** Solve these equations.
(a) $x(x + 5) = 0$ (b) $(x - 3)(x + 2) = 0$ (c) $(2x + 3)(x - 1) = 0$

**5** (a) Expand and simplify $(2x - 5)(x + 3)$.
(b) (i) Factorise $x^2 + 6x - 7$.
(ii) Solve the equation $x^2 + 6x - 7 = 0$.

Edexcel

**6** Solve these equations.
(a) $x^2 - 3x = 0$ (b) $x^2 - 3x + 2 = 0$ (c) $x^2 + x - 6 = 0$ (d) $x^2 - 11x + 28 = 0$

**7** (a) Factorise $2x^2 - 5x - 3 = 0$.
(b) Hence, solve the equation $2x^2 - 5x - 3 = 0$.

**8** Solve the equation $3x^2 - x - 2 = 0$.

**9** (a) Factorise. (i) $2x^2 - 7x + 3$ (ii) $4x^2 - 9$
(b) Solve. (i) $(3x + 2)(2x + 1) = 0$ (ii) $(3x + 2)(2x + 1) = 1$

Edexcel

**10** Express in the form $x^2 + bx + c = 0$ the quadratic equation which has solutions $x = 2$ and $x = -3$.

**11** (a) Write $x^2 - 4x - 8$ in the form $(x + a)^2 + b$.
(b) Hence, solve the equation $x^2 - 4x - 8 = 0$, correct to 2 decimal places.

**12** Solve the equation $(2x - 3)^2 = 100$.

Edexcel

**13** Solve the equation $x^2 + 3x - 5 = 0$.

**14** Find the solutions of the equation $x^2 - 4x - 1 = 0$.
Give your solutions correct to 3 d.p.

Edexcel

**15** Solve the equation $x^2 = 3x + 5$, giving your answers correct to 3 significant figures.

**16** Solve the equation $2x^2 - x - 2 = 0$.

**17** The area of a rectangle, with dimensions $x$ cm by $(x + 2)$ cm, is $18$ cm².
Calculate the value of $x$, correct to one decimal place.

## What you need to know

- A pair of **simultaneous equations** has the same unknown letters in each equation.

- To solve a pair of simultaneous equations find values for the unknown letters that fit **both** equations.

- Simultaneous equations can be solved either **graphically** or **algebraically**.

- Solving simultaneous equations **graphically** involves:
  drawing the graphs of both equations,
  finding the point(s) where the graphs cross.
  When the graphs of both equations are parallel, the equations have no solution.

  **Eg 1** Solve the simultaneous equations $x + 2y = 5$ and $x - 2y = 1$ graphically.

  Draw the graph of $x + 2y = 5$.
  Draw the graph of $x - 2y = 1$.

  The lines cross at the point $(3, 1)$.
  This gives the solution $x = 3$ and $y = 1$.

- Solving simultaneous equations **algebraically** involves using either:
  the **elimination** method, or the **substitution** method.

  **Eg 2** Solve the simultaneous equations $5x + 2y = 11$ and $3x - 4y = 4$ algebraically.

  $$5x + 2y = 11 \quad \text{A}$$
  $$3x - 4y = 4 \quad \text{B}$$

  A × 2 gives $\quad 10x + 4y = 22 \quad$ C $\qquad$ | To make the number of $y$'s the same
  $\qquad\qquad\qquad 3x - 4y = 4 \quad$ D $\qquad$ | we can multiply equation A by 2.

  C + D gives $\qquad\qquad 13x = 26 \qquad$ | The number of $y$'s is the **same** but the **signs** are **different**.
  $\qquad\qquad\qquad\quad x = 2 \qquad$ | To eliminate the $y$'s the equations must be **added**.

  Substitute $x = 2$ into $5x + 2y = 11$.
  $$10 + 2y = 11$$
  $$2y = 1$$
  $$y = 0.5 \qquad$$ | You can check the solution by substituting
  The solution is $x = 2$ and $y = 0.5$. | $x = 2$ and $y = 0.5$ into $3x - 4y = 4$.

- You should be able to solve simultaneous equations in which one equation is linear and one is quadratic.

  **Eg 3** Solve the simultaneous equations $y = x - 2$ and $x^2 + 3y = 12$.

  Substitute $y = x - 2$ into $x^2 + 3y = 12$. $\qquad$ | Using $y = x - 2$.
  $x^2 + 3(x - 2) = 12$ $\qquad\qquad$ | When $x = -6$. $\qquad$ When $x = 3$.
  $x^2 + 3x - 18 = 0$ $\qquad\qquad$ | $y = -6 - 2$ $\qquad\qquad$ $y = 3 - 2$
  $(x + 6)(x - 3) = 0$ $\qquad\qquad$ | $y = -8$ $\qquad\qquad\qquad$ $y = 1$
  $x = -6$ or $x = 3$

  This gives the solution: $x = -6$, $y = -8$ **and** $x = 3$, $y = 1$.

**1** (a) On the same axes, draw the graphs of $y + x = 4$ and $y - 3x = 2$
for values of $x$ from $-2$ to $2$.
(b) Hence, solve the simultaneous equations $y + x = 4$ and $y - 3x = 2$.

**2** Solve graphically the simultaneous equations $y = 3 - x$ and $y = x - 2$.

**3** (a) On the same axes, draw the graphs of $x + y = 4$ and $y = x + 2$.
(b) Use the graphs to solve the simultaneous equations $x + y = 4$ and $y = x + 2$. Edexcel

**4** The sketch shows the graph of $y = 2x - 1$.
Copy the diagram.

(a) On your diagram, sketch the graph of $y = 2x + 1$.
(b) Explain why the equations $y = 2x - 1$ and $y = 2x + 1$
cannot be solved simultaneously.

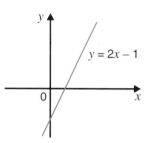

**5** Solve these simultaneous equations. $6x + y = 7$
$2x - y = -3$

**6** Solve the simultaneous equations $x + 3y = 13$ and $4x + 2y = 2$.

**7** Solve the simultaneous equations. $3x + y = 13$
$2x - 3y = 16$ Edexcel

**8** Heather sold 40 boxes of cards to raise money for charity.
She sold $x$ small boxes at £4 each and $y$ large boxes at £7 each.
She raised £184 altogether.
(a) Write down two equations connecting $x$ and $y$.
(b) Solve these simultaneous equations to find how many of each size of box she sold.

**9** Micro-scooters costs £$x$ each and pogo sticks cost £$y$ each.
2 micro-scooters and 4 pogo sticks cost £65.
1 micro-scooter and 3 pogo sticks cost £40.
(a) Write down two equations connecting $x$ and $y$.
(b) Solve these simultaneous equations to find the cost of a micro-scooter and a pogo stick.

**10** Solve these simultaneous equations. $2x + 5y = -1$ and $6x - y = 5$ Edexcel

**11** Solve the simultaneous equations $2x + 3y = 7$ and $3x - 2y = 17$.

**12** Use a graphical method to solve each of these pairs of simultaneous equations.
(a) $y = 4 - 2x$        (b) $y - x = 4$        (c) $y = 2x$
$y = x^2 - 4$                $y = 6x - x^2$            $x^2 + y^2 = 25$

**13** Use an algebraic method to solve the simultaneous equations $5y = 2x - 7$ and $xy = 6$.

**14** Solve the simultaneous equations.
(a) $y - x = -11$        (b) $y = 3 - x$        (c) $2x + y = 3$
$x^2 = y + 13$                $x^2 + y^2 = 17$            $y = \dfrac{1}{x}$

**15** (a) Factorise $x^2 - 4y^2$.
(b) Solve the simultaneous equations. $x^2 - 4y^2 = 24$
$x + 2y = 6$ Edexcel

**What you need to know**

● An **identity** is true for all values of $x$. It is the same expression written in another form.
For example:   $(2x + 3)^2 + (2x + 9)(2x + 5) = 2(4x^2 + 20x + 27)$.

> To show that an identity is true, either:
> start with the LHS and show that it is equal to the RHS, or
> start with the RHS and show that it is equal to the LHS.

● **Algebraic fractions** have a numerator and a denominator.

> To write an algebraic fraction in its **simplest form**:
> factorise the numerator and denominator of the fraction, divide
> the numerator and denominator by their highest common factor.

**Eg 1** Simplify.

(a) $\dfrac{2x - 4}{x^2 - 2x} = \dfrac{2(x - 2)}{x(x - 2)} = \dfrac{2}{x}$

(b) $\dfrac{x^2 - 9}{x^2 + 2x - 3} = \dfrac{(x + 3)(x - 3)}{(x + 3)(x - 1)} = \dfrac{(x - 3)}{(x - 1)}$

> The same methods used for adding,
> subtracting, multiplying and
> dividing numeric fractions can be
> applied to algebraic fractions.

(c) $\dfrac{2}{x - 3} - \dfrac{1}{x} = \dfrac{2x - (x - 3)}{x(x - 3)} = \dfrac{x + 3}{x(x - 3)}$

● You should be able to solve equations involving algebraic fractions.

● The solutions to a variety of equations can be found using a process called **iteration**.

> The process of iteration has three stages.
> **1.** Rearranging an equation to form an **iterative formula**.
> **2.** Choosing a **starting value**, $x_1$.
> **3.** **Substituting** the starting value, and then values of $x_n$ into the iterative formula.
> Continuing the process until the required degree of accuracy is obtained.

**Eg 2** Find a solution to the equation   $x^2 - 4x - 3 = 0$,   correct to 2 decimal places,
using iteration.

Use the iterative formula   $x_{n+1} = \sqrt{4x_n + 3}$.

$$x_1 = 4$$
$$x_2 = \sqrt{4 \times 4 + 3} \qquad\qquad = 4.3588\ldots$$
$$x_3 = \sqrt{4 \times 4.3588\ldots + 3} = 4.5205\ldots$$
$$x_4 = \sqrt{4 \times 4.5205\ldots + 3} = 4.5915\ldots$$
$$x_5 = \sqrt{4 \times 4.5915\ldots + 3} = 4.6223\ldots$$
$$x_6 = \sqrt{4 \times 4.6223\ldots + 3} = 4.6356\ldots$$
$$x_7 = \sqrt{4 \times 4.6356\ldots + 3} = 4.6414\ldots$$
$$x_8 = \sqrt{4 \times 4.6414\ldots + 3} = 4.6438\ldots$$

$$x = 4.64, \text{ correct to 2 d.p.}$$

- **Trial and improvement** is a method used to solve equations. The accuracy of the value of the unknown letter is improved until the required degree of accuracy is obtained.

**Eg 3** Use a trial and improvement method to find a solution to the equation $x^3 + x = 40$, correct to one decimal place.

| $x$ | $x^3 + x$ | Comment |
|---|---|---|
| 3 | $27 + 3 = 30$ | Too small |
| 4 | $64 + 4 = 68$ | Too big |
| 3.5 | $42.8... + 3.5 = 46.3...$ | Too big |
| 3.3 | $35.9... + 3.3 = 39.2...$ | Too small |
| 3.35 | $37.5... + 3.35 = 40.9...$ | Too big |

For accuracy to 1 d.p. check the second decimal place. The solution lies between 3.3 and 3.35.

$x = 3.3$, correct to 1 d.p.

## Exercise 21

**1** Expand and simplify $(x + 3)^2 - (x - 3)^2$.

**2** Show that $2x(x + y) - (x + y)^2 = x^2 - y^2$.

**3** (a) By expanding both sides, or otherwise, show that
$$(m^2 + 1)(n^2 + 1) = (m + n)^2 + (mn - 1)^2.$$
(b) Using this result, or otherwise, write 500 050 as the sum of 2 square numbers. *Edexcel*

**4** Simplify. (a) $\dfrac{x^2 - 3x}{x}$  (b) $\dfrac{2x^2 - 6x}{4x - 12}$  (c) $\dfrac{x^2 + 2x + 1}{x^2 - 2x - 3}$  (d) $\dfrac{x^2 + x}{x^2 - 1}$

**5** Simplify. (a) $\dfrac{1}{x} + \dfrac{1}{2x}$  (b) $\dfrac{2x}{x + 1} + \dfrac{1}{2}$  (c) $\dfrac{1}{x + 2} + \dfrac{2}{2x - 5}$

**6** (a) Show that $y = \dfrac{3}{2x - 1} - \dfrac{2}{x + 3}$ can be written as $y = \dfrac{11 - x}{2x^2 + 5x - 3}$.
(b) Hence, find the values of $x$ when $y = 1$, correct to 2 decimal places.

**7** (a) Express $\dfrac{1}{x - 2} + \dfrac{2}{x + 4}$ as a single algebraic fraction.
(b) Hence, or otherwise, solve $\dfrac{1}{x - 2} + \dfrac{2}{x + 4} = \dfrac{1}{3}$. *Edexcel*

**8** Solve the equation $\dfrac{x}{2} - \dfrac{3}{x + 5} = 1$.

**9** Solve the equation $\dfrac{2}{2x - 1} - 1 = \dfrac{2}{x + 1}$.

**10** (a) (i) Factorise $3x^2 - 8x - 3$.
(ii) Hence, or otherwise, simplify $\dfrac{9x^2 - 1}{3x^2 - 8x - 3}$.
(b) Solve the equation $\dfrac{1}{1 - x} - \dfrac{1}{1 + x} = 1$.

**11** A solution to the equation $x^2 - 2x - 10 = 0$ may be found by using the iteration $x_{n+1} = \sqrt{(2x_n + 10)}$.
(a) Starting with $x_1 = 4$, calculate $x_2$.
Write down all the figures on your calculator display.
(b) Continue this iteration until there is no change in the second decimal place.
Write down all the figures shown on your calculator for each value of $x_n$. *Edexcel*

**12** Use a trial and improvement method to solve the equation $x^3 + x^2 = 300$.
Show all your trials. Give your answer correct to one decimal place.

# Transforming Graphs

## What you need to know

- **Function notation** is a way of expressing a relationship between two variables.
  For example

  Input, $x$ ⟶ | function, f<br>e.g. *cube* | ⟶ Output, f($x$)

  This notation gives $f(x) = x^3$

  f($x$) means 'a function of $x$'.
  In the example above, $f(x) = x^3$ is equivalent to the equation $y = x^3$ where $y = f(x)$.

- **Transformations**, such as **translations** and **stretches**, can be used to change the position and size of a graph.
  The equation of the transformed (new) graph is related to the equation of the original graph.

**In general**

| Original | New graph | Transformation | Note |
|---|---|---|---|
| $y = f(x)$ | $y = f(x) + a$ | **translation**, vector $\begin{pmatrix} 0 \\ a \end{pmatrix}$. | If $a$ is **positive**, curve moves $a$ units **up**.<br>If $a$ is **negative**, curve moves $a$ units **down**. |
| $y = f(x)$ | $y = f(x + a)$ | **translation**, vector $\begin{pmatrix} -a \\ 0 \end{pmatrix}$. | If $a$ is **positive**, curve moves $a$ units **left**.<br>If $a$ is **negative**, curve moves $a$ units **right**. |
| $y = f(x)$ | $y = af(x)$ | **stretch**, from the $x$ axis, parallel to the $y$ axis, scale factor $a$. | The $y$ coordinates on the graph of $y = f(x)$ are **multiplied** by $a$. |
| $y = f(x)$ | $y = f(ax)$ | **stretch**, from the $y$ axis, parallel to the $x$ axis, scale factor $\frac{1}{a}$. | The $x$ coordinates on the graph of $y = f(x)$ are **divided** by $a$. |
| $y = f(x)$ | $y = -f(x)$ | **reflection** in the $x$ axis. | The $y$ coordinates on the graph of $y = f(x)$ **change signs**. |
| $y = f(x)$ | $y = f(-x)$ | **reflection** in the $y$ axis. | The $x$ coordinates on the graph of $y = f(x)$ **change signs**. |

**Eg 1** The diagram shows the graph of $y = f(x)$.
Draw the graphs of $y = f(x - 2)$ and $y = f(x) - 2$.

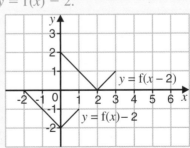

- You should be able to draw a suitable graph to find the relationship between a given set of variables.
  **Linear functions** have straight line graphs, such as $y = ax + b$.
  From the graph of **$y$ against $x$**, the gradient $= a$ and the $y$-intercept $= b$.
  **Non-linear functions**, such as $y = ax^n + b$, can be written as the linear function $y = az + b$ by substituting $z = x^n$.
  From the graph of **$y$ against $x^n$**, the gradient $= a$ and the $y$-intercept $= b$.

**1** The graph of $y = f(x)$ for $-2 \leqslant x \leqslant 2$ is shown.
On separate diagrams draw the graphs of $y = f(x)$ and:

  (a) $y = f(x + 2)$,     (b) $y = f(x) + 2$,

  (c) $y = 2f(x)$,     (d) $y = -f(x)$.

**2** The diagram shows a sketch of the graph of $y = f(x)$ for $-2 \leqslant x \leqslant 2$.

Each of the graphs below is a transformation of this graph.
Write down the equation of each graph.

  (a)

  (b)

  (c)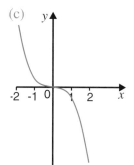

**3** The graph of $y = f(x)$ is shown in the diagram.

  (a) Copy $y = f(x)$ and sketch the graph of $y = f(x - 3)$
    on the same axes.

  (b) Copy $y = f(x)$ and sketch the graph of $y = f(x) - 4$
    on the same axes.

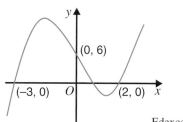

Edexcel

**4** The table shows the results of an experiment.

| $x$ | 5 | 12 | 20 | 24 |
|---|---|---|---|---|
| $y$ | 5.5 | 6.9 | 8.5 | 9.3 |

  (a) Draw a graph to show these results.
  (b) The results are connected by the equation $y = ax + b$.
    Find this equation and hence find the value of $x$ when $y = 20$.

**5** The diagram represents a tray.
The base of the tray is a square with sides $x$ cm long.
The sides of the tray are 2 cm high.
The weight, $W$ grams, of the tray is given by the formula
$W = ax^2 + bx$ where $a$ and $b$ are constants.
The values of $W$ for some values of $x$ are shown in the table.

| $x$ | 5 | 10 | 15 | 20 | 25 |
|---|---|---|---|---|---|
| $W$ | 34 | 122 | 260 | 450 | 690 |

  (a) Work out the values of $\dfrac{W}{x}$ and use the values to plot a graph of $\dfrac{W}{x}$ against $x$.

  (b) Use your graph to estimate the values of $a$ and $b$.

The base of a tray is a square with sides 50 cm long.
  (c) Calculate an estimate of the weight of this tray.

Edexcel

**Transforming Graphs**

# Algebra
# Non-calculator Paper

Do not use a calculator for this exercise.

**1** (a) Simplify (i) $5c + 2c - 3c$, (ii) $5p - 8r + 12r - 6p$.
(b) Find the value of (i) $5x + 2y$ when $x = 3$ and $y = 6$,
(ii) $4g - 2h$ when $g = 2$ and $h = -4$.
Edexcel

**2** (a) Copy and complete this table of values for $y = 3x - 1$.

| $x$ | $-3$ | $-2$ | $-1$ | $0$ | $1$ | $2$ | $3$ |
|---|---|---|---|---|---|---|---|
| $y$ | $-10$ | | $-4$ | | | $5$ | |

(b) Draw the graph of $y = 3x - 1$.
(c) Use your graph to find the value of $x$ when $y = 6.5$.
Edexcel

**3** A sequence begins $1$, $-1$, ... This rule is used to continue the sequence.

> Multiply the last number by 2 and then subtract 3.

(a) What is the next term in the sequence?
(b) A term in the sequence is called $x$. Write, in terms of $x$, the next term in the sequence.

**4** Multiply out $5(3x - 2)$.
Edexcel

**5** Choc Bars cost 27 pence each.
Write down a formula for the cost, $C$ pence, of $n$ Choc Bars.
Edexcel

**6** Hannah is $x$ years old.
(a) Her sister Louisa is 3 years younger than Hannah.
Write an expression, in terms of $x$, for Louisa's age.
(b) Their mother is four times as old as Hannah.
Write an expression, in terms of $x$, for their mother's age.
(c) The total of their ages is 45 years.
By forming an equation in $x$, find their ages.

**7** Factorise $9x + 12$.
Edexcel

**8** (a) Factorise $k^2 - 2k$.
(b) Solve (i) $3 - 4x = x + 8$, (ii) $3(2x + 1) = 6$.

**9** Given that $s = 2t^3$, find the value of $t$ when $s = 250$.

**10** $y = \frac{4}{5}(9 - x)$. Find the value of $x$ when $y = 6$.

**11** Solve the equation $\frac{3x - 5}{8} = 5$.
Edexcel

**12** $-2 < x \leqslant 1$. $x$ is an integer. Write down all the possible values of $x$.
Edexcel

**13** The fraction, $p$, of an adult's dose of medicine which should be given to a child who
weighs $w$ kg is given by the formula $p = \frac{3w + 20}{200}$.

A child weighs 35 kg.
(a) Work out the fraction of an adult's dose which should be given to this child.
Give your answer as a fraction in its simplest form.

(b) Use the formula $p = \frac{3w + 20}{200}$ to find the weight of a child whose dose is the same as
an adult's dose.
Edexcel

**14** Here are the first five numbers of a simple number sequence.   1,   5,   9,   13,   17,   …
Write down, in terms of $n$, the $n$ th term in this sequence.

Edexcel

**15** (a)   Solve the inequality   $3x < 8 - x$   and show the solution on a number line.
(b)   List all the values of $n$, where $n$ is an integer, such that   $-3 < 2n + 1 \leqslant 3$.

**16** Match these equations to their graphs.

**A**   $y = x$
**B**   $y + x = 1$
**C**   $y = x^2$
**D**   $y = x^3$

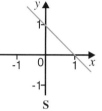

P            Q            R            S

**17** (a)   Copy and complete the table of values for   $y = x^2 - 2x + 1$.

| $x$ | $-1$ | 0 | 1 | 2 | 3 |
|---|---|---|---|---|---|
| $y$ | | 1 | 0 | | 4 |

(b)   Draw the graph of   $y = x^2 - 2x + 1$   for values of $x$ from $-1$ to 3.
(c)   Use your graph to solve the equations
    (i)   $x^2 - 2x + 1 = 0$,        (ii)   $x^2 - 2x + 1 = 2$.

**18** Water is poured into a container at a constant rate.
Copy the axes given and sketch the graph of the
depth of the water against time as the container is filled.

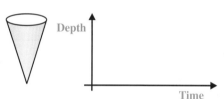

**19** Expand and simplify   $3(2x - 1) - 2(2x - 3)$.

Edexcel

**20** $v = u - ft$
(a)   Express $t$ in terms of $u$, $v$ and $f$.
(b)   When   $u = 10$   and   $v = 2$,   write down the formula for $t$ in terms of $f$.
(c)   Given that   $1 \leqslant f \leqslant 10$,   and that $t$ is a **whole number**, use your answer to (b)
        to write down all the possible values of $t$.

Edexcel

**21** The line with equation   $3y = -2x + 6$   has been drawn on the grid.
(a)   Copy the diagram and draw the graph of   $y = 2x - 2$
        on the same grid.
(b)   Use the graphs to find the solution of the
        simultaneous equations   $3y = -2x + 6$   and   $y = 2x - 2$.
A line is drawn parallel to   $3y = -2x + 6$   through the point (2, 1).
(c)   Find the equation of this line.

Edexcel

**22** (a)   Simplify.   (i)   $\dfrac{p^6}{p^2}$        (ii)   $q^3 \times q$        (iii)   $(x^3)^2$
(b)   Simplify   (i)   $3a^2 \times 2a^2b^3$,        (ii)   $(2a^2)^{-3}$.
(c)   Factorise completely   $9x^2y - 6xy^3$.

Edexcel

**23** (a)   Work out the value of   $x^2 - 5x + 6$   when   $x = -2$.
(b)   (i)   Factorise   $x^2 - 5x + 6$.
        (ii)   Hence, solve the equation   $x^2 - 5x + 6 = 0$.

**24** (a)   Solve the equations   (i)   $x(x + 2) = 0$,        (ii)   $y^2 - 3y + 2 = 0$.
(b)   Expand and simplify   $(2x - 3)(x + 2)$.

**25** Here is the graph of $y = f(x)$.

(a) Copy the graph of $y = f(x)$ and sketch the graph of $y = f(x + 2)$ on the same axes.

(b) Copy the graph of $y = f(x)$ and sketch the graph of $y = 2f(x)$ on the same axes.

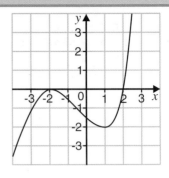

Edexcel

**26** Simplify. (a) $(3x^2y)^3$ (b) $\dfrac{3a^2b^3 \times 4a^5b}{6a^3b^2}$

**27** Factorise the following. (a) $3x^2 - 75$ (b) $3x^2 - 8x + 5$

**28** (a) Factorise $p^2 - q^2$.

(b) Here is a sequence of numbers: 0, 3, 8, 15, 24, 35, 48, …
An expression for the $n$th term of this sequence is $n^2 - 1$.
Show algebraically that the product of **any** two consecutive terms of the sequence can be written as the product of four consecutive integers.

Edexcel

**29** On separate diagrams, sketch the graphs of:

(a) $x^2 + y^2 = 9$, (b) $y = 2^x$, for $-3 \leqslant x \leqslant 3$.

**30** $y$ is directly proportional to the square root of $x$. When $x = 25$ then $y = 15$.

(a) Work out a formula to connect $x$ and $y$.

(b) Work out the value of $x$ when $y = 6$.

Edexcel

**31** (a) Show that $(2x + 3)^2 - (2x + 1)^2 = 8(x + 1)$.

(b) Hence, solve the equation $(2x + 3)^2 - (2x + 1)^2 = x^2 - 1$.

**32** Rearrange the equation $x = \dfrac{y - 5}{3 - y}$ to make $y$ the subject.

**33** The speed-time graph of an underground train travelling between two stations is shown.

(a) What is the maximum speed of the train?

(b) Calculate the acceleration of the train.

(c) Calculate the distance between the stations.

**34** Find the equation of the line which is perpendicular to $2y + x = 6$ and goes through the point (4, 1).

**35** A transformation has been applied to the graph of $y = x^2$ to give the graph of $y = -x^2$.

(a) Describe fully the transformation.

For all values of $x$, $x^2 + 4x = (x + p)^2 + q$.

(b) Find the values of $p$ and $q$.

A transformation has been applied to the graph of $y = x^2$ to give the graph of $y = x^2 + 4x$.

(c) Using your answer to part (b), or otherwise, describe fully the transformation. Edexcel

**36** Solve the simultaneous equations $y = 2x + 1$ and $xy = 3$.

**37** You are given that $\dfrac{1}{x + 1} - \dfrac{3}{2x - 1} = 2$. Show that $4x^2 + 3x + 2 = 0$.

# Algebra
# Calculator Paper

You may use a calculator for this exercise.

**1** (a) Simplify (i) $x + x + x$    (ii) $2a + 4b + a - 2b$    (iii) $3(a + 2)$

    (b) Expand and simplify $2(x - 1) + 3(2x + 1)$     Edexcel

**2** Here is a formula for working out a printing cost.

| printing cost | = | price per sheet of paper | × | number of sheets of paper | + | fixed charge |

The price per sheet of paper is £0.04. 2500 sheets of paper are used.
The fixed charge is £45.50.
Work out the printing cost.     Edexcel

**3** The graph shows the journey of a cyclist from Cordy to Dalton and back.

(a) On the way to Dalton, the cyclist stopped for a rest.
For how long did the cyclist stop?

(b) During which part of the journey did the cyclist travel the fastest? Explain your answer.

(c) What was the average speed of the cyclist from Dalton back to Cordy?

**4** Solve (a) $4p + 6 = 26$,    (b) $5(2q + 6) = 25$,    (c) $18y - 27 = 10y - 25$.   Edexcel

**5** (a) Draw the line $y = 2x + 1$ for values of $x$ from $-1$ to $2$.

    (b) The line $y = 2x + 1$ crosses the line $x = -5$ at $P$.
Give the coordinates of $P$.

**6** Here is a rule to change kilograms to pounds.

> Multiply the number of kilograms by 22 and then divide by 10.

(a) Use the rule to change 5 kilograms to pounds.

(b) Write a formula to change $K$ kilograms to $L$ pounds.

(c) Use your formula to find the value of $K$ when $L = 55$.

**7** (a) Expand. $t(t - 2)$    (b) Factorise. $3y - 12$     Edexcel

**8** (a) Solve the equations (i) $4(a - 2) = 6$,    (ii) $5t + 3 = -1 + t$.

    (b) The sum of the numbers $x$, $x - 3$ and $x + 7$ is 25.
By forming an equation in $x$, find the value of $x$.

**9** The equation $x^3 - 15x = 31$ has a solution between 4 and 5.
Use a trial and improvement method to find this solution.
Give your answer correct to one decimal place. You must show **ALL** your working.   Edexcel

**10** (a) Simplify (i) $x^6 \div x^2$      (ii) $y^4 \times y^4$.

(b) Expand and simplify $(t + 4)(t - 2)$.

(c) Write down the integer values of $x$ that satisfy the inequality $-2 \leqslant x < 4$.     Edexcel

**11** (a) Here are the first four terms of a simple sequence.   5,   11,   17,   23

Write, in terms of $n$, the $n$th term of the sequence.

(b) The $n$th term of another sequence is $n^2 + 3$.

Write down the first and second terms of the sequence.

**12** A shop sells Big lollipops at 80p each and Small lollipops at 60p each.

Henry buys $x$ Big lollipops.

(a) Write down an expression, in terms of $x$, for the cost of Henry's lollipops.

Lucy buys $r$ Big lollipops and $t$ Small lollipops.

(b) Write down an expression, in terms of $r$ and $t$, for the total cost of Lucy's lollipops.

The cost of $g$ Big lollipops and 2 Small lollipops is £10.80.

(c) (i) Write this as an equation in terms of $g$.

(ii) Use your equation to find the value of $g$.     Edexcel

**13** Make $x$ the subject of the formula $y = 2x - 5$.

**14** (a) Write down the equations of the lines labelled **A**, **B** and **C** in the diagram.

(b) Write down three inequalities to describe the shaded region.

**15**

The volume, $V$, of the barrel is given by the formula: $V = \dfrac{\pi H(2R^2 + r^2)}{3000}$.

$\pi = 3.14$,   $H = 60$,   $R = 25$   and   $r = 20$.

Calculate the value of $V$.

Give your answer correct to 3 significant figures.

Edexcel

**16** The dimensions of a rectangle are shown.

The rectangle has an area of $104\,\text{cm}^2$.

Form an equation for the area of the rectangle and show that it can be written in the form $2x^2 + x - 105 = 0$.

$(2x - 1)$ cm

$(x + 1)$ cm

**17** (a) Expand $x(x + 4)$.

(b) Solve the simultaneous equations $x + 8y = 5$ and $3x - 4y = 8$.

**18** You are given the formula $y = \sqrt{\dfrac{2x}{5}}$.

(a) Find the value of $y$ when $x = 3.6 \times 10^{-4}$.

(b) Rearrange the formula to give $x$ in terms of $y$.

**19** The diagram shows points $A(2, 0)$, $B(0, 2)$ and $C(3, 5)$.

Find the equations of the line segments.

(a) $AB$,      (b) $BC$,      (c) $AC$.

$\bullet\, C\,(3, 5)$

$B\,(0, 2)\,\bullet$

$A\,(2, 0)$

**20** Solve the equation $\dfrac{5x - 3}{3} - \dfrac{1 + 2x}{2} = 3$.

**21** The graph of a function has been sketched for $0 < x \leqslant 10$.
The equation of the function is **one** of the following:

$$y = kx^3 \quad \textbf{or} \quad y = kx^2 \quad \textbf{or} \quad y = \frac{k}{x}$$

where $k$ is a positive constant.
By choosing the appropriate equation and using the point (6, 2)
which lies on the curve, calculate the value of $k$.

Edexcel

**22**

(a) The graph of a straight line is shown.
What is the equation of the line?

(b) The equation of a different line is $4y - 3x = 8$.
What is the gradient of this line?

**23** $y$ is proportional to the square root of $x$ and $y = 2.4$ when $x = 0.25$.
Find the value of $x$ when $y = 60$.

**24** Solve the equation $x^2 + 2x - 5 = 0$.
Give your answers correct to two decimal places.

**25** The volumes of these cuboids are the same.

(a) Show that $3x^2 + 2x - 12 = 0$.

(b) By solving the equation
$3x^2 + 2x - 12 = 0$, find the value of $x$.
Give your answer correct to one decimal place.

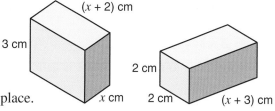

**26** (a) Draw the graph of $y = 3 - 2x^2$ for values of $x$ between $-2$ and $2$.

(b) Use your graph to solve these equations. (i) $3 - 2x^2 = 0$ (ii) $3 - 2x^2 = x$

(c) A student wants to use the graph to solve the equation $2x^2 - x - 2 = 0$.
What is the equation of the line that needs to be drawn?

**27** Solve the equation $2x^2 = 5x - 1$.

**28** You are given that $y = 8x^n$ and that $y = 1$ when $x = 2$.
Find the value of $n$.

**29** (a) Simplify fully the expression $\dfrac{2x^2 - 18}{2x^2 - 4x - 6}$.

(b) You are given the equation $xy = x + y$.
Rearrange the equation to give a formula for $y$ in terms of $x$.

(c) You are given that $(2x - b)^2 - 5 = ax^2 - 4x + c$ for all values of $x$.
Find the values of $a$, $b$ and $c$.

**30** Solve the simultaneous equations $x + y = 4$ and $y = x^2 + 2x$.

**31** A solution of $x^3 + x^2 - 4 = 0$ may be found by using the iteration $x_{n+1} = \dfrac{2}{\sqrt{(x_n + 1)}}$.

(a) Use $x_1 = 1$ to calculate $x_2$.

(b) Continue with this iteration until you find a solution of $x^3 + x^2 - 4 = 0$ to 2 d.p.

Edexcel

**32** (a) You are given that $(x + p)^2 + q = x^2 - 4x + 7$.
Find the values of $p$ and $q$.

(b) Rearrange the equation $y(x - 3) = 1 + 2x$ to give a formula for $x$ in terms of $y$.

**33** Solve the equation $\dfrac{2}{x-1} - \dfrac{1}{x+1} = 1$.

# Angles and 2-D Shapes

## What you need to know

- Types and names of angles.

| **Acute angle** | **Right angle** | **Obtuse angle** | **Reflex angle** |
|---|---|---|---|
|  |  |  |  |
| $0° < a < 90°$ | $a = 90°$ | $90° < a < 180°$ | $180° < a < 360°$ |

- Angle properties.

| **Angles at a point** | **Complementary angles** | **Supplementary angles** | **Vertically opposite angles** |
|---|---|---|---|
|  |  |  |  |
| $a + b + c = 360°$ | $x + y = 90°$ | $a + b = 180°$ | $a = c$ and $b = d$ |

- A straight line joining two points is called a **line segment**.

- Lines which meet at right angles are **perpendicular** to each other.

- Lines which never meet and are always the same distance apart are **parallel**.

- When two parallel lines are crossed by a **transversal** the following pairs of angles are formed.

| **Corresponding angles** | **Alternate angles** | **Allied angles** |
|---|---|---|
|  |  |  |
| $a = c$ | $b = c$ | $b + d = 180°$ |

> Arrowheads are used to show that lines are **parallel**.

- A **triangle** is a shape made by three straight sides.

- Triangles can be:  **acute-angled** (all angles less than 90°),
  **obtuse-angled** (one angle greater than 90°),
  **right-angled** (one angle equal to 90°).

- The sum of the angles in a triangle is 180°.
  $a + b + c = 180°$

- The exterior angle is equal to the sum of the two opposite interior angles.  $a + b = d$

- Types of triangle:

| **Scalene** | **Isosceles** | **Equilateral** |
|---|---|---|
| |  | |

> A **sketch** is used when an accurate drawing is not required. Dashes across lines show sides that are equal in length. Equal angles are marked using arcs.

- A two-dimensional shape has **line symmetry** if the line divides the shape so that one side fits exactly over the other.

- A two-dimensional shape has **rotational symmetry** if it fits into a copy of its outline as it is rotated through 360°.

- A shape is only described as having rotational symmetry if the order of rotational symmetry is 2 or more.

- The number of times a shape fits into its outline in a single turn is the **order of rotational symmetry**.

Order of rotational symmetry 5

- A **quadrilateral** is a shape made by four straight lines.

- The sum of the angles in a quadrilateral is 360°.

- Facts about these special quadrilaterals:

rectangle   square   parallelogram   rhombus   trapezium   isosceles trapezium   kite

| Quadrilateral | Sides | Angles | Diagonals | Line symmetry | Order of rotational symmetry |
|---|---|---|---|---|---|
| **Rectangle** | Opposite sides equal and parallel | All 90° | Bisect each other | 2 | 2 |
| **Square** | 4 equal sides, opposite sides parallel | All 90° | Bisect each other at 90° | 4 | 4 |
| **Parallelogram** | Opposite sides equal and parallel | Opposite angles equal | Bisect each other | 0 | 2 |
| **Rhombus** | 4 equal sides, opposite sides parallel | Opposite angles equal | Bisect each other at 90° | 2 | 2 |
| **Trapezium** | 1 pair of parallel sides | | | | |
| **Isosceles trapezium** | 1 pair of parallel sides, non-parallel sides equal | 2 pairs of equal angles | Equal in length | 1 | 1* |
| **Kite** | 2 pairs of adjacent sides equal | 1 pair of opposite angles equal | One bisects the other at 90° | 1 | 1* |

*A shape is only described as having rotational symmetry if the order of rotational symmetry is 2 or more.

- A **polygon** is a many-sided shape made by straight lines.

- A polygon with all sides equal and all angles equal is called a **regular polygon**.

- Shapes you need to know:   A 5-sided polygon is called a **pentagon**.
  A 6-sided polygon is called a **hexagon**.
  An 8-sided polygon is called an **octagon**.

- The sum of the exterior angles of any polygon is 360°.

- At each vertex of a polygon:   interior angle + exterior angle = 180°

- The sum of the interior angles of an $n$-sided polygon is given by:
  $(n - 2) \times 180°$

- For a regular $n$-sided polygon:   exterior angle $= \dfrac{360°}{n}$

- A shape will **tessellate** if it covers a surface without overlapping and leaves no gaps.

interior angle   exterior angle

**1** Find the size of the lettered angles. Give a reason for each answer.

(a)

(b)

(c)

**2** Find the size of the lettered angles.

(a)

(b)

(c)

**3** (a) Copy the diagram.
Shade two more squares so that the final diagram has line symmetry only.

(b) Make another copy of the diagram.
Shade two more squares so that the final diagram
has rotational symmetry only.

**4**

The diagram shows a quadrilateral *ABCD*.
*AB* = *BC*  and  *CD* = *DA*.

Angle *ADC* = 36°  and  angle *BCD* = 105°.
Work out the size of angle *ABC*.

**5** *ABCD* is a quadrilateral.
*AB* = 6 cm,  *AC* = 9 cm,  *BC* = 5 cm,  *AD* = 3.5 cm  and  angle *BAD* = 66°.
Make an accurate drawing of the quadrilateral *ABCD*.

Edexcel

**6** *ABCDEFGH* is a regular octagon.
*O* is the centre of the octagon.

Calculate the size of angle *AOF*.

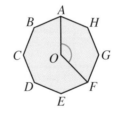

Edexcel

**7** (a) A regular polygon has 9 sides.
Find the size of an interior angle.

(b) A regular polygon has an exterior angle of 20°.
Show that the sum of the interior angles is 2880°.

**8**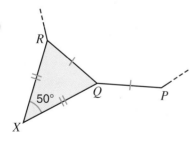

*PQ* and *QR* are two sides of a regular 10-sided polygon.
*QRX* is an isosceles triangle with *RX* = *XQ*.
Angle *QXR* = 50°.

Work out the size of the obtuse angle *PQX*.

**9** *ABC* is an equilateral triangle.
*AC* and *CD* are two sides of a regular polygon
and *BC* and *CD* are two sides of an identical polygon.
How many sides has each of these polygons?

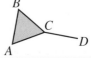

# Circle Properties

## What you need to know

- A **circle** is the shape drawn by keeping a pencil the same distance from a fixed point on a piece of paper.

- You should know the meaning of the words shown on the diagrams below.

- The vertices of a **cyclic quadrilateral** lie on the circumference of a circle.

- **Circle properties**

The angle in a semi-circle is a right angle.

Angles in the same segment are equal.

$x = 2y$
The angle at the centre is twice the angle at the circumference.

$p + r = 180°$ and $q + s = 180°$
Opposite angles of a cyclic quadrilateral are supplementary.

A tangent is perpendicular to the radius at the point of contact.

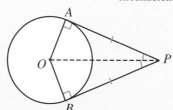

Tangents drawn to a circle from the same point are equal.

The angle between a tangent and a chord is equal to any angle in the alternate (opposite) segment.

- You should be able to use circle properties to solve problems.

$O$ is the centre of the circle. Find the marked angles.
$a = 43°$ (angles in the same segment)
$b = 2 \times 43°$ ($\angle$ at centre = twice $\angle$ at circum.)
$b = 86°$
$c = 180° - 43°$ (opp. $\angle$'s of a cyclic quad)
$c = 137°$

**You should be able to prove that:**
- the angle at the centre is twice the angle at the circumference,
- the angle in a semi-circle is a right angle,
- angles in the same segment are equal,
- opposite angles of a cyclic quadrilateral are supplementary,
- the angle between a tangent and a chord is equal to any angle in the alternate segment.

**1** O is the centre of the circle.
Work out the size of the lettered angles. Give a reason for each of your answers.

(a)   (b)   (c)   (d)

**2** O is the centre of the circle. Work out the size of angle x.

**3**

BC, AB and AC are tangents to
the circle at D, E, F respectively.
Calculate the size of angle EDF,
showing your reasoning carefully.

*Edexcel*

**4** AXB is a tangent to the circle, centre O.
Find the size of the angles marked a, b and c.

**5**

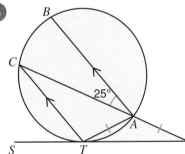

A, B, C and T are points on
the circumference of a circle.
Angle BAC = 25°.
The line PTS is the tangent at T to the circle.
AT = AP.   AB is parallel to TC.
(a) Calculate the size of angle APT.
    Give reasons for your answer.
(b) Calculate the size of angle BTS.
    Give reasons for your answer.

*Edexcel*

**6** A, B, C, D and E are points on the circumference of a circle.
SAT is the tangent to the circle at A.
AB = BC.   AE is parallel to CD.   Angle ECD = 48°.
(a) Calculate the size of angle ABC.
(b) Calculate the size of angle TAB.

*Edexcel*

**7**

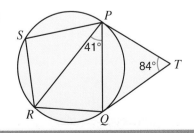

TP and TQ are tangents to a circle, as shown.
PQRS is a cyclic quadrilateral.
Angle PTQ = 84°   and   angle QPR = 41°.
(a) Showing your working and stating your reasons,
    calculate  (i)  angle QRP,     (ii)  angle PSR.
(b) Is PR a diameter of the circle?
    Explain your answer.

*Edexcel*

# Perimeters and Areas

## What you need to know

- **Perimeter** is the distance round the outside of a shape.
- **Area** is the amount of surface covered by a shape.
- You should be able to use these formulae to find areas.

**Triangle:** $A = \frac{1}{2} \times b \times h$    **Rectangle:** $A = lb$    **Parallelogram:** $A = bh$    **Trapezium:** $A = \frac{1}{2}(a + b)h$

**Eg 1** Calculate the area of this triangle.

$A = \frac{1}{2} \times b \times h$

$A = \frac{1}{2} \times 6 \times 4 \, \text{cm}^2$

$A = 12 \, \text{cm}^2$

**Eg 2** Find the area of this trapezium.

$A = \frac{1}{2}(a + b)h$

$A = \frac{1}{2}(6 + 9)5$

$A = \frac{1}{2} \times 15 \times 5$

$A = 37.5 \, \text{cm}^2$

- You should be able to calculate **lengths** and **areas** associated with **circles**.

> **Circumference** of a circle is given by: $C = \pi d$   or   $C = 2\pi r$
> **Area** of a circle is given by: $A = \pi r^2$
>
> The **lengths of arcs** and the **areas of sectors** are proportional to the angle at the centre of the circle.
>     For a sector with angle $a°$
>
> **Length of arc** $= \dfrac{a}{360} \times \pi d$
>
> **Area of sector** $= \dfrac{a}{360} \times \pi r^2$
>
>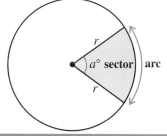

Take $\pi$ to be 3.14 or use the $\pi$ key on your calculator.

**Eg 3** Find the circumference of a circle with radius 9 cm.
Give your answer to 1 d.p.

$C = 2 \times \pi \times r$
$C = 2 \times \pi \times 9$
$C = 56.548\ldots$
$C = 56.5 \, \text{cm}$, correct to 1 d.p.

**Eg 4** Find the area of a circle with radius 6 cm.
Give your answer to 3 sig. figs.

$A = \pi \times r^2$
$A = \pi \times 6 \times 6$
$A = 113.097\ldots$
$A = 113 \, \text{cm}^2$, correct to 3 sig. figs.

**Eg 5** A circle has a circumference of 25.2 cm. Find the diameter of the circle.

$C = \pi d$,   so,   $d = \dfrac{C}{\pi}$

$d = \dfrac{25.2}{\pi}$

$d = 8.021\ldots$
$d = 8.0 \, \text{cm}$, correct to 1 d.p.

**Eg 6** A circle has an area of 154 cm². Find the radius of the circle.

$A = \pi r^2$,   so,   $r^2 = \dfrac{A}{\pi}$

$r^2 = \dfrac{154}{\pi} = 49.019\ldots$

$r = \sqrt{49.019\ldots} = 7.001\ldots$
$r = 7 \, \text{cm}$, to the nearest cm.

**Eg 7**  *OAB* is a sector of a circle of radius 7.2 cm.  Angle *AOB* = 50°.
Calculate   (a)   the length of arc *AB*,
            (b)   the area of sector *AOB*.

(a)   Length of arc $= \frac{a}{360} \times \pi d = \frac{50}{360} \times \pi \times 14.4$

$= 6.2831... = 6.28$ cm, correct to 3 s.f.

(b)   Area of sector $= \frac{a}{360} \times \pi r^2 = \frac{50}{360} \times \pi \times 7.2^2$

$= 22.619... = 22.6$ cm², correct to 3 s.f.

● Shapes formed by joining different shapes together are called **compound shapes**.
To find the area of a compound shape we must first divide the shape up into rectangles,
triangles, circles, etc., and find the area of each part.

**Eg 8**  Find the area of this metal plate.

The plate can be divided into a rectangle, *A*, and a semi-circle, *B*.
Area *A* = 3.6 × 4.2 = 15.12 cm²
Area *B* = $\frac{1}{2} \times \pi \times 1.8^2 = 5.089...$ cm²
Total area = 15.12 + 5.089... = 20.2 cm², correct to 3 s.f.

## Exercise 25

Take π to be 3.14 or use the π key on your calculator.

**1**  This diagram shows the floor plan of a room.
Work out the area of the floor.

Edexcel

**2**  The perimeter of this rectangle is 22 cm.
The length of the rectangle is 8 cm.
Work out the area of the rectangle.

8 cm

Edexcel

**3**  Calculate the area of triangle *PQR*.

**4**  The diagram shows a trapezium, *PQRS*.
Calculate the area of the trapezium.

*P*  5.5 cm  *Q*
7 cm
*S*  9.5 cm  *R*

**5**  A circle has a radius of 32 cm.
Work out the circumference of the circle.
Give your answer correct to the nearest centimetre.

Edexcel

**6**  Tranter has completed three-fifths of a circular jigsaw puzzle.
The puzzle has a radius of 20 cm.
What area of the puzzle is complete?

**7** Triangle *XYZ* has an area of 12 cm².
*XZ* = 5 cm.
Calculate *YP*.

**8**

The diagram shows a circle of diameter 70 cm
inside a square of side 70 cm.
Work out the area of the shaded part of the diagram.

Edexcel

**9** A rectangular carpet is twice as long as it is wide. The carpet covers an area of 24.5 m².
Calculate the length of the carpet.

**10** A mat is made in the shape of a rectangle with a semi-circle added at one end.
The width of the mat is 1.52 metres.
The length of the mat is 1.86 metres.
Calculate the area of the mat.
Give your answer in square metres,
correct to 2 decimal places.

Edexcel

**11**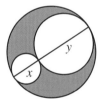

A table has a top in the shape of a circle with a radius of 45 centimetres.
(a)   Calculate the area of the circular table top.

The base of the table is also in the shape of a circle.
The circumference of this circle is 110 centimetres.
(b)   Calculate the diameter of the base of the table.

Edexcel

**12** Three circles overlap, as shown.
The largest circle has a diameter of 12 cm.
The ratio of the diameters *x* : *y* is 1 : 2.
Calculate the shaded area.
Give your answer in terms of $\pi$.

**13** A circle has an area of 100 cm².
Calculate the circumference of the circle.
Give your answer correct to three significant figures.

**14** Alfie says,   *"A semi-circle with a radius of 10 cm has a larger area than
a whole circle with half the radius."*
Is he correct?
You **must** show working to justify your answer.

**15** A wiper blade on a windscreen cleans the area shown.

Calculate the area of windscreen cleaned by the wiper.
Give your answer in terms of $\pi$.

**16** A circle, of radius 5.6 cm, is cut into two sectors.
The areas of the sectors are in the ratio 2 : 3.
Calculate the area and perimeter of the smaller sector.
Give your answer correct to a suitable degree of accuracy.

**17** The area of a sector of a circle is 32 cm². The diameter of the circle is 13 cm.
Calculate the perimeter of the sector.

*Perimeters and Areas*

# Maps, Loci and Constructions

## What you need to know

- **Compass points** and **three-figure bearings** are used to describe direction.
- A **bearing** is an angle measured from the North line in a clockwise direction.
- A bearing can be any angle from 0° to 360° and is written as a three-figure number.
- To find a bearing:   measure angle $a$ to find the bearing of $Y$ from $X$,
  measure angle $b$ to find the bearing of $X$ from $Y$.

- **Scales**
  The distances between points on a map are all drawn to the same scale.
  There are two ways to describe a scale.
  1. A scale of 1 cm to 10 km means that a distance of 1 cm on the map represents an actual distance of 10 km.
  2. A scale of 1 : 10 000 means that all distances measured on the map have to be multiplied by 10 000 to find the real distance.
- The path of a point which moves according to a rule is called a **locus**.
- The word **loci** is used when we talk about more than one locus.
- You should be able to draw the locus of a point which moves according to a given rule.

**Eg 1**  A ball is rolled along this zig-zag.
Draw the locus of $P$, the centre of the ball,
as it is rolled along.

**Using a ruler and compasses you should be able to:**
- Construct the **perpendicular from a point to a line**.
- Construct the **perpendicular from a point on a line**.
- Construct the **perpendicular bisector of a line**.

Points on the line $CD$ are **equidistant** from the points $A$ and $B$.

- Construct the **bisector of an angle**.

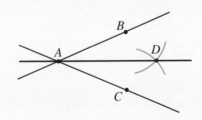

Points on the line $AD$ are **equidistant** from the lines $AB$ and $AC$.

- You should be able to solve loci problems which involve using these constructions.

**Eg 2**  $P$ is a point inside triangle $ABC$ such that:
(i)   $P$ is equidistant from points $A$ and $B$,
(ii)  $P$ is equidistant from lines $AB$ and $BC$.
Find the position of $P$.

> To find point $P$:
> (i)  construct the perpendicular bisector of line $AB$,
> (ii) construct the bisector of angle $ABC$.

$P$ is at the point where these lines intersect.

① The diagram shows a sketch of the course to be used for a running event.

(a) Draw an accurate plan of the course, using a scale of 1 cm to represent 100 m.

(b) Use your plan to find
 (i) the bearing of X from Y,
 (ii) the distance XY in metres.

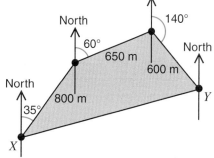

② The ball is rolled along the zig-zag.
Copy the diagram and draw the locus of the centre of the ball as it is rolled from X to Y.

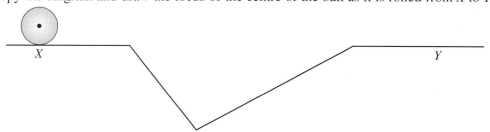

③ The diagram represents a box which is to be moved across a floor, XY.

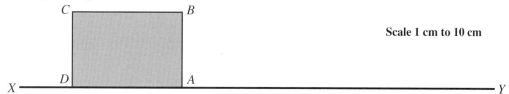

**Scale 1 cm to 10 cm**

$AD = 30$ cm and $AB = 20$ cm.
First the box is rotated about the point A so that BC becomes vertical.
Then the box is rotated about the new position of the point B so that CD becomes vertical.
(a) Copy the diagram and make a scale drawing of the locus of the point C.
(b) Find the maximum height of C above the floor.                     Edexcel

④ Use ruler and compasses to **construct** an equilateral triangle with sides of length 4 cm.
You must show all construction lines.                     Edexcel

⑤ Copy the diagram and use ruler and compasses to **construct** the perpendicular to the line segment, AB, that passes through the point, P.
You must show all construction lines.

Edexcel

⑥ (a) Construct a kite PQRS in which  $PQ = PS = 7$ cm,  $QR = RS = 5$ cm
  and the diagonal  $QS = 6$ cm.
  X is a point inside the kite such that:
  (i)  X is equidistant from P and Q,
  (ii)  X is equidistant from sides PQ and PS.
(b) By constructing the loci for (i) and (ii) find the position of X.
(c) Measure the distance PX.

# Transformations

## What you need to know

- The movement of a shape from one position to another is called a **transformation**.

- **Single transformations** can be described in terms of a reflection, a rotation, a translation or an enlargement.

- **Reflection**: The image of the shape is the same distance from the mirror line as the original.

- **Rotation**: All points are turned through the same angle about the same point, called a centre of rotation.

- **Translation**: All points are moved the same distance in the same direction without turning.

- **Enlargement**: All lengths are multiplied by a scale factor.

$$\text{Scale factor} = \frac{\text{new length}}{\text{original length}}$$   | New length = scale factor × original length |

The size of the original shape is:
        **increased** by using a scale factor greater than 1,
        **reduced** by using a scale factor which is a fraction, i.e. between 0 and 1.
When a shape is enlarged using a **negative scale factor** the image is **inverted**.

- You should be able to draw the transformation of a shape.

**Eg 1**  Draw the image of triangle $P$ after it has been translated with vector $\begin{pmatrix} -3 \\ 2 \end{pmatrix}$.

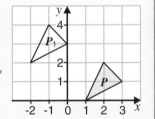

- You should be able to fully describe transformations.

| Transformation | Image same shape and size? | Details needed to describe the transformation |
|---|---|---|
| Reflection | Yes | Mirror line, sometimes given as an equation. |
| Rotation | Yes | Centre of rotation, amount of turn, direction of turn. |
| Translation | Yes | Horizontal movement and vertical movement. Vector: top number = horizontal movement, bottom number = vertical movement. |
| Enlargement | No | Centre of enlargement, scale factor. |

**Eg 2**  Describe the single transformation which maps
    (a)  $A$ onto $B$,
    (b)  $A$ onto $C$,
    (c)  $A$ onto $D$,
    (d)  $D$ onto $E$,
    (e)  $E$ onto $F$.

    (a)  **Reflection** in the line $x = 3$.
    (b)  **Rotation** of $180°$ about $(2, 1)$.

    (c)  **Translation** with vector $\begin{pmatrix} 2 \\ -3 \end{pmatrix}$.

    (d)  **Enlargement** scale factor 2, centre $(2, 0)$.

    (e)  **Enlargement** scale factor $-\frac{1}{2}$, centre $(6, -2)$.

1. The diagram shows the positions of kites *P*, *Q*, *R* and *S*.

   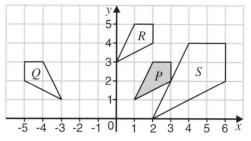

   (a) (i) *P* is mapped onto *Q* by a reflection.
   What is the equation of the
   line of reflection?

   (ii) *P* is mapped onto *R* by a translation.
   What is the vector of the translation?

   (iii) *P* is mapped onto *S* by an enlargement.
   What is the centre and scale factor of
   the enlargement?

   (b) *P* is mapped onto *T* by a rotation through 90° clockwise about $(1, -2)$.
   On squared paper, copy *P* and draw the position of *T*.

2. In each diagram, *A* is mapped onto *B* by a single transformation. Describe each transformation.

   (a)

   (b)

   (c)

   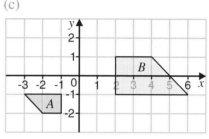

3. Triangle *X* has vertices $(1, 2)$, $(0, 3)$, $(-1, 1)$.
   Triangle *Y* has vertices $(3, 0)$, $(2, 1)$, $(1, -1)$.
   Describe the single transformation which maps *X* onto *Y*.

4. The diagram shows triangles ***T***, ***S*** and ***U***.

   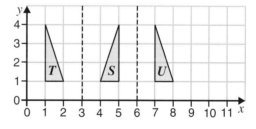

   ***S*** is the image of ***T*** under a reflection in
   the line $x = 3$.

   ***U*** is the image of ***S*** under a reflection in
   the line $x = 6$.

   A reflection in the line $x = 3n$,
   where *n* is an integer, is denoted by $R_n$.

   So, ***S*** is the image of ***T*** under $R_1$ and ***U*** is the image of ***T*** under $R_1$, followed by $R_2$.

   ***V*** is the image of ***T*** under the successive transformations $R_1$, followed by $R_2$, followed by $R_3$.

   (a) Copy the diagram and draw ***V***.

   (b) Describe fully the single transformation that will map ***T*** to ***V***.

   ***W*** is the image of ***T*** under the successive transformations $R_1$, followed by $R_2$, followed by $R_3$,
   and so on to $R_n$.

   (c) Describe fully the single transformation that will map ***T*** to ***W***
   (i) when *n* is even,   (ii) when *n* is odd.   Edexcel

5. Triangle *PQR* has vertices $P(2, -3)$, $Q(-2, -5)$, $R(-4, -3)$.
   On squared paper, draw and label triangle *PQR*.

   (a) Enlarge triangle *PQR* by scale factor $\frac{1}{2}$ from the centre of enlargement $(4, -1)$.
   Label the image *A*.

   (b) Rotate triangle *PQR* through 180° about the point $(-2, -1)$.
   Label the image *B*.

   (c) Describe fully the single transformation which maps triangle *A* onto triangle *B*.

# Pythagoras' Theorem

 What you need to know

- The longest side in a right-angled triangle is called the **hypotenuse**.

- The **Theorem of Pythagoras** states:
  "In any right-angled triangle the square on the hypotenuse is equal to the sum of the squares on the other two sides."
  $$a^2 = b^2 + c^2$$

- When we know the lengths of two sides of a right-angled triangle, we can use the Theorem of Pythagoras to find the length of the third side.

$a^2 = b^2 + c^2$
Rearranging gives:  $b^2 = a^2 - c^2$
$c^2 = a^2 - b^2$

**Eg 1**  Calculate the length of side $a$.

$a^2 = b^2 + c^2$
$a^2 = 8^2 + 3^2$
$a^2 = 64 + 9 = 73$
$a = \sqrt{73} = 8.544...$
$a = 8.5\,\text{cm}$, correct to 1 d.p.

**Eg 2**  Calculate the length of side $b$.

$b^2 = a^2 - c^2$
$b^2 = 9^2 - 7^2$
$b^2 = 81 - 49 = 32$
$b = \sqrt{32} = 5.656...$
$b = 5.7\,\text{cm}$, correct to 1 d.p.

---

**Exercise 28**  Do not use a calculator for questions 1 and 2.

**1**  $ABC$ is a right-angled triangle.
$AB = 5\,\text{cm}$  and  $AC = 12\,\text{cm}$.
Calculate the length of $BC$.

**2**

The diagram shows the cross-section of the roof of a house.
The width of the house, $PR$, is $10\,\text{m}$.
$QR = 6\,\text{m}$  and  angle $PQR = 90°$.
Calculate the length of $PQ$.

**3**  The diagram shows a rectangular sheet of paper.
The paper is $20\,\text{cm}$ wide and the diagonal, $d$, is $35\,\text{cm}$.

Calculate the length of the sheet of paper.

**4** Calculate the length of the line joining the points $A(-2, -3)$ and $B(6, 1)$.

**5**

Is $PQR$: an acute-angled triangle,
an obtuse-angled triangle,
or a right-angled triangle?

Show your calculations and state your conclusions.

**6** $AB = 19.5$ cm, $AC = 19.5$ cm and $BC = 16.4$ cm.
Angle $ADB = 90°$.
$BDC$ is a straight line.

Calculate the length of $AD$.
Give your answer in centimetres, correct to 1 decimal place.

Edexcel

**7**

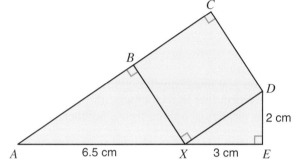

In the diagram, $BCDX$ is a square.
$AXE$ is a straight line with $AX = 6.5$ cm
and $XE = 3$ cm. $DE = 2$ cm.

(a) Calculate the area of $BCDX$.
(b) Calculate the length of $AB$,
correct to one decimal place.

**8** The diagram shows a rectangle drawn inside a circle.
The centre of the circle is at $O$.
The rectangle is 15 cm long and 9 cm wide.

Calculate the circumference of the circle.
Give your answer correct to 3 significant figures.

Edexcel

**9**

A cuboid has dimensions 20 cm by 10 cm by 5 cm.

Calculate the length of the diagonal $AB$.
Give your answer to a suitable degree of accuracy.

**10** The diagram shows a square-based pyramid.
The edges $PA = PB = PC = PD = 9$ cm.
$X$ is at the centre of the base $ABCD$.
$PX = 8$ cm.

Calculate the area of the base, $ABCD$.

## What you need to know

- **Trigonometry** is used to find the lengths of sides and the sizes of angles in right-angled triangles.

- You must learn the **sine**, **cosine** and **tangent** ratios.

$$\sin a = \frac{\text{opposite}}{\text{hypotenuse}} \qquad \cos a = \frac{\text{adjacent}}{\text{hypotenuse}} \qquad \tan a = \frac{\text{opposite}}{\text{adjacent}}$$

- Each ratio links the size of an angle with the lengths of two sides. If we are given the values for two of these we can find the value of the third.

- When we look **up** from the horizontal the angle we turn through is called the **angle of elevation**.

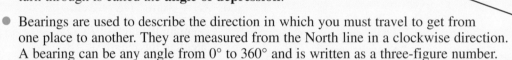

- When we look **down** from the horizontal the angle we turn through is called the **angle of depression**.

- Bearings are used to describe the direction in which you must travel to get from one place to another. They are measured from the North line in a clockwise direction. A bearing can be any angle from 0° to 360° and is written as a three-figure number.

- You should be able to use trigonometry to find the lengths of sides and the sizes of angles when solving problems involving right-angled triangles.

**Eg 1** Find the length, $d$.

$$\tan a = \frac{\text{opp}}{\text{adj}}$$
$$\tan 62° = \frac{d}{6.6}$$
$$d = 6.6 \times \tan 62°$$
$$d = 12.412\ldots$$
$$d = 12.4 \text{ m, correct to 3 s.f.}$$

**Eg 2** Find the size of angle $a$.

$$\sin a = \frac{\text{opp}}{\text{hyp}}$$
$$\sin a° = \frac{11}{16}$$
$$a = \sin^{-1} \frac{11}{16}$$
$$a = 43.432\ldots$$
$$a = 43.4°, \text{ correct to 1 d.p.}$$

- When working in three dimensions the first task is to identify the length, or angle, that you are trying to find.
  The length, or angle, will always form part of a triangle together with either:
  two other sides of known length, or
  one side of known length and an angle of known size.
  Sometimes, more than one triangle is needed to solve a problem.

- A straight line meets a plane at a **point**.
  The angle *XPT* is the **angle between the line and the plane**.
  The line *XT* is perpendicular to the plane.

**1** In the right-angled triangle shown:
$\sin y = 0.8$ and $\cos y = 0.6$
Find the value of $x$.

**2** The diagram shows a house and a garage on level ground.
A ladder is placed with one end at the bottom of the house wall.
The top of the ladder touches the top of the garage wall.
The distance between the garage wall and the house is 1.4 m.
The angle the ladder makes with the ground is 62°.

(a) Calculate the height of the garage wall.
Give your answer correct to 3 significant figures.

A ladder of length 3.5 m is then placed against the house wall.
The bottom of this ladder rests against the bottom of the garage wall.

(b) Calculate the angle that this ladder makes with the ground.
Give your answer correct to 1 decimal place.

*Edexcel*

**3** Abbi is standing on level ground, at $B$, a distance
of 19 m away from the foot, $E$, of a tree, $TE$.
She measures the angle of elevation of the top
of the tree, at a height of 1.55 m above the
ground, as 32°.

Calculate the height, $TE$, of the tree.

*Edexcel*

**4**

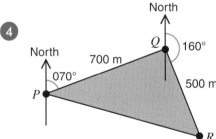

The diagram shows the path of a jet-ski from $P$ to $Q$ to $R$.

$Q$ is 700 m from $P$ on a bearing of 070°.
$R$ is 500 m from $Q$ on a bearing of 160°.

Calculate the bearing of $P$ from $R$.

**5** $XABCD$ is a pyramid on a square base of side 8 cm.
$XA = XB = XC = XD = 9$ cm.

(a) Calculate $XO$, the perpendicular height of the pyramid.
(b) Find the angle between $XC$ and the base.

**6**

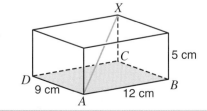

A cuboid has dimensions 12 cm by 9 cm by 5 cm.

Calculate the angle between the diagonal $XA$ and the
base $ABCD$.

Trigonometry . . . Trigonometry . . .

- **You should be able to:**
- find the number of **faces**, **edges** and **vertices** of a 3-D shape,
- draw the **net** of a 3-D shape,
- use **isometric** paper to make a 2-D drawing of a 3-D shape.

- A **plane of symmetry** slices through a 3-D shape so that one half is the mirror image of the other half.

- Three-dimensional shapes can have **axes of symmetry**.

- **Plans and Elevations**
  The view of a 3-D shape looking from above is called a **plan**.
  The view of a 3-D shape from the front or sides is called an **elevation**.

  **Eg 1** Draw diagrams to show the plan and elevation from **X**, for this 3-dimensional shape.

X     plan     elevation X

Dotted lines are used to show hidden edges.

- **Volume** is the amount of space occupied by a 3-D shape.

- The formula for the volume of a **cuboid** is:
  Volume = length × breadth × height
  $V = l \times b \times h$

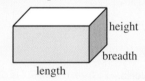

height

breadth

length

- Volume of a **cube** is:  $V = l^3$

- To find the **surface area** of a cuboid, find the areas of the 6 rectangular faces and add the answers together.

- **Prisms**
  If you make a cut at right angles to the length of a prism you will always get the same cross-section.

  **Triangular prism**

cross-section

length

- Volume of a prism = area of cross-section × length

  **Eg 2** Calculate the volume of this prism.
  The cross-section of this prism is a trapezium.

  Area of cross-section $= \frac{1}{2}(5 + 3) \times 2.5$

  $\qquad\qquad\qquad\quad = 4 \times 2.5$

  $\qquad\qquad\qquad\quad = 10\,\text{cm}^2$

  Volume of prism = area of cross-section × length
  $\qquad\qquad\quad = 10 \times 12$
  $\qquad\qquad\quad = 120\,\text{cm}^3$

5 cm

3 cm

2.5 cm     12 cm

- A **cylinder** is a prism.
  Volume of a cylinder is:     Volume $= \pi \times r^2 \times h$
  Surface area of a cylinder is:   Surface area $= 2\pi r^2 + 2\pi rh$

r

h

**Eg 3** A cylinder has a radius of 4 cm and a height of 6 cm.
Calculate (a) the volume and (b) the surface area of the cylinder.

(a) $V = \pi r^2 h$
$= \pi \times 4 \times 4 \times 6$
$= 301.592\ldots$
$= 302\text{ cm}^3$,
    correct to 3 s.f.

(b) Surface area $= 2\pi r^2 + 2\pi rh$
$= 2 \times \pi \times 4 \times 4 + 2 \times \pi \times 4 \times 6$
$= 100.53\ldots + 150.796\ldots$
$= 251\text{ cm}^2$,
    correct to 3 s.f.

● These formulae are used in calculations involving **cones**, **pyramids** and **spheres**.

**Cone**

$V = \frac{1}{3} \times$ base area $\times$ height

$V = \frac{1}{3} \pi r^2 h$

Curved surface area $= \pi r l$

**Pyramid**

$V = \frac{1}{3} \times$ base area $\times$ height

**Sphere**

Volume $= \frac{4}{3} \pi r^3$

Surface area $= 4\pi r^2$

**Eg 4** A cone is 6.4 cm high and has a
radius of 4.8 cm.
Calculate the curved surface area
of the cone.

Slant height, $l = \sqrt{6.4^2 + 4.8^2}$
$= \sqrt{64} = 8\text{ cm}$

Curved surface area is given by:
$\pi r l = \pi \times 4.8 \times 8 = 120.637\ldots$
$= 120.6\text{ cm}^2$, correct to 1 d.p.

**Eg 5** A steel ball has a radius of 4 cm.
Calculate (a) the volume,
(b) the surface area of the ball.

(a) Volume $= \frac{4}{3} \pi r^3 = \frac{4}{3} \times \pi \times 4^3$
$= 268.082\ldots$
$= 268\text{ cm}^3$, correct to 3 s.f.

(b) Surface area $= 4\pi r^2 = 4 \times \pi \times 4^2$
$= 201.061\ldots$
$= 201\text{ cm}^2$, correct to 3 s.f.

● A **frustum of a cone** is formed by removing the
top of a cone with a cut parallel to its circular base.

**Exercise 30** Do not use a calculator for questions 1 to 5.

**1** The diagram shows a square-based pyramid.
(a) How many planes of symmetry has the pyramid?
(b) How many axes of symmetry has the pyramid?

**2**
The diagram shows a solid drawn on isometric paper.
(a) Draw the plan of the solid.
(b) Draw the elevation of the solid from the direction
shown by the arrow.

**3** (a) Which of these cuboids has the larger volume?
Show all your working.
(b) Which cuboid has the larger surface area?

**A**

**B**

**4** A cuboid has a volume of 100 cm³. The cuboid is 8 cm long and 5 cm wide.
Calculate the surface area of the cuboid.

**5** A cylinder has a radius of 6 cm and a height of 5 cm.
Calculate the volume of the cylinder. Give your answer in terms of $\pi$.

**6** The diagram shows a cylinder.
The height of the cylinder is 26.3 cm.
The diameter of the base of the cylinder is 8.6 cm.
Calculate the volume of the cylinder.
Give your answer correct to 3 significant figures.

Edexcel

**7**

The diagram shows a triangular prism.

$BC = 4$ cm, $CF = 12$ cm and angle $ABC = 90°$.

The volume of the triangular prism is 84 cm³.
Work out the length of the side $AB$ of the prism.

Edexcel

**8** A cylindrical water tank has radius 40 cm and height 90 cm.
(a) Calculate the total surface area of the tank.

A full tank of water is used to fill a paddling pool.
(b) The paddling pool is a cylinder with diameter 2.4 metres.
Calculate the depth of water in the pool.

**9** A cylinder has a height of 10 cm and a radius of 4 cm. The cylinder is solid.
Calculate the **total** surface area of the cylinder.

Edexcel

**10**

A tent has a groundsheet as its horizontal base.
The shape of the tent is a triangular prism of length 8 metres,
with two identical half right-circular cones, one at each end.
The vertical cross-section of the prism is an isosceles triangle
of height 2.4 metres and base 3.6 metres.

(a) Calculate the area of the groundsheet.
(b) Calculate the total volume of the tent.

Edexcel

**11** A cone is 10 cm high and has a base radius of 6 cm.
(a) Calculate the curved surface area of the cone.

The top of the cone is cut off to leave a frustum 8 cm high.
(b) Calculate the volume of the frustum.

**12**

Rachel buys a ball in a box. The ball touches each side of the box.
The box is a cube with sides of length 20 cm.
(a) Calculate the difference between the volume of the box and
the volume of the ball.
(b) Calculate the difference between the surface area of the box
and the surface area of the ball.

**13** The diagram shows a triangular pyramid.

Angle $ABC = 90°$, $AB = 5$ cm and $BC = 3$ cm.

The volume of the pyramid is 28 cm³.
Calculate the height of the pyramid.

# Understanding and Using Measures

## What you need to know

- The common units – both **metric** and **imperial** – used to measure **length**, **mass** and **capacity**.

- How to convert from one unit to another. This includes knowing the connection between one metric unit and another and the approximate equivalents between metric and imperial units.

| Metric Units | Imperial Units | Conversions |
|---|---|---|
| **Length**<br>1 kilometre (km) = 1000 metres (m)<br>1 m = 100 centimetres (cm)<br>1 cm = 10 millimetres (mm)<br><br>**Mass**<br>1 tonne (t) = 1000 kilograms (kg)<br>1 kg = 1000 grams (g)<br><br>**Capacity and volume**<br>1 litre = 1000 millilitres (ml)<br>1 cm³ = 1 ml | **Length**<br>1 foot = 12 inches<br>1 yard = 3 feet<br><br>**Mass**<br>1 pound = 16 ounces<br>14 pounds = 1 stone<br><br>**Capacity and volume**<br>1 gallon = 8 pints | **Length**<br>5 miles is about 8 km<br>1 inch is about 2.5 cm<br>1 foot is about 30 cm<br><br>**Mass**<br>1 kg is about 2.2 pounds<br><br>**Capacity and volume**<br>1 litre is about 1.75 pints<br>1 gallon is about 4.5 litres |

- How to change between units of area.   For example $1\,m^2 = 10\,000\,cm^2$.

- How to change between units of volume.   For example $1\,m^3 = 1\,000\,000\,cm^3$.

- You should be able to recognise limitations on the accuracy of measurements.
  A **discrete measure** can only take a particular value and a **continuous measure** lies within a range of possible values which depends upon the degree of accuracy of the measurement.

> If a **continuous measure**, $c$, is recorded to the nearest $x$, then the limits of the possible values of $c$ can be written as   $c \pm \frac{1}{2}x$.

**Eg 1** A log is 12 m in length. The length is correct to the nearest metre.
What is the minimum length of the log?   Minimum length = 12 − 0.5 = 11.5 m

**Eg 2** A road is 400 m long, to the nearest 10 m.
Between what lengths is the actual length of the road?
Actual length = 400 m ± 5 m   395 m ⩽ actual length < 405 m

**Eg 3** A punnet of strawberries weighs 2.4 kg, correct to the nearest 100 g.
Between what limits must the weight of the strawberries lie?
Actual weight = 2.4 kg ± 0.05 kg
Lower limit   = 2.35 kg
Upper limit   = 2.45 kg
So,   2.35 kg ⩽ actual weight < 2.45 kg.

- By analysing the **dimensions** of a formula it is possible to decide whether a given formula represents a **length** (dimension 1), an **area** (dimension 2) or a **volume** (dimension 3).

**Eg 4** $p, q, r$ and $s$ represent lengths.
By using dimensions, decide whether the expression $pq + qr + rs$ could represent a perimeter, an area or a volume.
Writing $pq + qr + rs$ using dimensions:
$$L \times L + L \times L + L \times L = L^2 + L^2 + L^2 = 3L^2$$
So, $pq + qr + rs$ has dimension 2 and could represent an area.

**1** On a map the distance between two hospitals is 14.5 cm.
The map has been drawn to a scale of 1 to 250 000.
Calculate the actual distance between the hospitals in kilometres.

**2** Debbie is 5 feet 4 inches tall and weighs 9 stone 2 lb. Joyce is 155 cm tall and weighs 60 kg.
Who is taller? Who is heavier? You must show your working.

**3** Last year Felicity drove 2760 miles on business.
Her car does 38 miles per gallon.
Petrol costs 89 pence per litre.
She is given a car allowance of 25 pence per kilometre.
How much of her car allowance is left after paying for her petrol?
Give your answer to the nearest £.

**4** (a) A beach towel is rectangular in shape and measures 1.8 m by 90 cm.
Calculate the area of the towel in square metres.
(b) Change $0.2 \, m^3$ to $cm^3$.

**5** Jafar has a piece of wood that has a length of 30 cm, correct to the nearest centimetre.
(a) Write down the minimum length of the piece of wood.

Fatima has a different piece of wood that has a length of 18.4 cm, correct to the nearest millimetre.
(b) Write down the maximum and minimum lengths between which the length of the piece of wood must lie.
Edexcel

**6** Some of the expressions shown in the table below can be used to calculate areas or volumes of various shapes.
$\pi$ and 2 are numbers which have no dimensions. The letters $r$, $b$ and $h$ represent lengths.

| $2\pi r$ | $\pi r^2$ | $2bh$ | $\pi r^3$ | $b^2 h$ | $r^2 + b^3$ |
|---|---|---|---|---|---|

(a) Which of these expressions can be used to calculate an area?
(b) Which of these expressions can be used to calculate a volume?
Edexcel

**7** Correct to 3 decimal places, $a = 2.236$.
(a) For this value of $a$, write down (i) the upper bound, (ii) the lower bound.

Correct to 3 decimal places, $b = 1.414$.
(b) Calculate (i) the upper bound for the value of $a + b$,
(ii) the lower bound for the value of $a + b$.
(c) Calculate the lower bound for the value of $ab$.
(d) Calculate the upper bound for the value of $\frac{a}{b}$.
Edexcel

**8** The measurements of a rectangular ticket are given as 5 cm by 3 cm, correct to the nearest centimetre.
(a) Between what limits must the width of the ticket lie?
(b) Between what limits must the area of the ticket lie?
(c) The area of the ticket is given as $(15 \pm x) \, cm^2$.
Suggest a suitable value for $x$.

**9** Michael rides his bicycle to work.
The diameter of each wheel is 65 cm, correct to the nearest centimetre.
The distance he cycles to work is 2.4 km, correct to one decimal place.
Calculate the least number of turns each wheel makes when Michael cycles to work.

**10** $x = 3$, correct to 1 significant figure.
$y = 0.06$, correct to 1 significant figure.
Calculate the greatest possible value of $y - \frac{x-7}{x}$.
Edexcel

# Congruent Triangles and Similar Figures

## What you need to know

- When two shapes are the same shape and size they are said to be **congruent**.

- There are four ways to show that a pair of triangles are congruent.

  | | |
  |---|---|
  | **SSS** 3 corresponding sides. | **ASA** 2 angles and a corresponding side. |
  | **SAS** 2 sides and the included angle. | **RHS** Right angle, hypotenuse and one other side. |

  **Eg 1**  Show that triangles $ABC$ and $XYZ$ are congruent.

  $AC = XZ$ (given)
  $AB = XY$ (given)
  $\angle BAC = \angle YXZ = 60°$ (sum of angles in $\Delta = 180°$)

  So, triangles $ABC$ and $XYZ$ are congruent (SAS).

- When two figures are **similar**:
  their **shapes** are the same, their **angles** are the same,
  corresponding **lengths** are in the same ratio,
  this ratio is the **scale factor** of the enlargement.

  $$\text{Scale factor} = \frac{\text{new length}}{\text{original length}}$$

- For **similar triangles**:
  corresponding lengths are opposite equal angles,
  the scale factor is the ratio of the
  corresponding sides.

  $$\frac{AB}{PQ} = \frac{BC}{QR} = \frac{CA}{RP} = \text{scale factor}$$

- You should be able to find corresponding lengths in similar triangles.

  **Eg 2**  These two triangles are similar.
  Find the lengths of the sides marked $x$ and $y$.

  $AB$ and $PQ$ are corresponding sides.
  Scale factor $= \dfrac{PQ}{AB} = \dfrac{5}{3}$

  $x = 4.5 \times \frac{5}{3} = 7.5\,\text{cm}$
  $y = 10 \div \frac{5}{3} = 6\,\text{cm}$

- You should be able to find corresponding lengths, areas and volumes in similar figures.

  When the **length** scale factor $= k$,  the **area** scale factor $= k^2$,  the **volume** scale factor $= k^3$.

  **Eg 3**  Two fish tanks are similar. The smaller tank is 12 cm high and holds 4 litres of water. The larger tank is 18 cm high. How many litres of water does it hold?

  Ratio of heights is    $12 : 18 = 2 : 3$.
  Ratio of volumes is   $2^3 : 3^3 = 8 : 27$.

  To find the ratio of volumes, cube the ratio of lengths.

  Water in larger tank $= 4 \times \frac{27}{8} = 13.5$ litres

The diagrams in this exercise have not been drawn accurately.

**1** Which two of these triangles are congruent to each other? Give a reason for your answer.

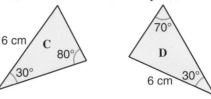

**2** The diagram shows rectangles **A**, **B** and **C**.

(a) Explain why rectangles **A** and **C** are **not** similar.

(b) Rectangles **A** and **B** are similar. Work out the length of rectangle **B**.

**3**

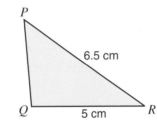

Triangle $ABC$ is similar to triangle $PQR$.
Angle $ABC$ = angle $PQR$.
Angle $ACB$ = angle $PRQ$.

Calculate the length of
(a) $PQ$,          (b) $AC$.

Edexcel

**4** In the diagram $ABC$ and $AED$ are straight lines.
$BE$ is parallel to $CD$.

(a) Explain why triangles $ABE$ and $ACD$ are similar.

$AB = 3.2\,\text{cm}$,   $BE = 3.6\,\text{cm}$,   $ED = 1.4\,\text{cm}$   and   $DC = 5.4\,\text{cm}$.

(b) Calculate
   (i) the length of $AC$,
   (ii) the length of $AE$.

**5**

These tops are similar.
The height of the small top is 6 cm.
The height of the large top is 9 cm.

(a) Find the ratio of the surface area of the small top to the surface area of the large top.
(b) The volume of the large top is 135 cm³.
   Calculate the volume of the small top.

**6** The diagram represents a 1 : 50 scale model of a church tower with a spire.
The tower is cylindrical and the spire is conical.

(a) Calculate the total volume, in cm³, of the model.
(b) Find the ratio of the volume of the scale model to the volume of the real tower and spire.
(c) Hence, or otherwise, calculate the total volume of the real tower and spire.
   Give your answer in m³.

Edexcel

## What you need to know

- Quantities which have both **size** and **direction** are called **vectors**.
  For example: **Displacement** – A combination of distance and direction.

- **Vector notation**
  Vectors can be represented by **column vectors** or by **directed line segments**.
  Vectors can be labelled using:
  > capital letters to indicate the start and finish of a vector,
  > bold lower case letters.

  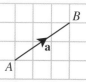

  In a **column vector:**
  > The top number describes the **horizontal** part of the movement.
  > The bottom number describes the **vertical** part of the movement.
  $$\overrightarrow{AB} = \mathbf{a} = \begin{pmatrix} 3 \\ 2 \end{pmatrix}$$

- Vectors are **equal** if they have the same length **and** they are in the same direction.
  Vectors **a** and $-\mathbf{a}$ have the same length **but** are in **opposite directions**.
  The vector $n\mathbf{a}$ is parallel to the vector **a**.
  The length of vector $n\mathbf{a} = n \times$ the length of vector **a**.

- **Vector addition**
  The combination of the displacement from $A$ to $B$ followed by the displacement from $B$ to $C$ is
  equivalent to a total displacement from $A$ to $C$.

  This can be written using vectors as $\overrightarrow{AB} + \overrightarrow{BC} = \overrightarrow{AC}$. $\overrightarrow{AC}$ is called the **resultant vector**.

- Combinations of vectors can be shown on **vector diagrams**.

  **Eg 1** **a** and **b** are shown. Draw vectors to represent $\mathbf{a} + \mathbf{b}$ and $\mathbf{a} - \mathbf{b}$.

- You should be able to use **vector geometry** to solve simple geometrical problems,
  which can often involve parallel lines.

  **Eg 2** $OAXB$ is a quadrilateral.

  $\overrightarrow{OA} = \mathbf{a}$, $\overrightarrow{OB} = \mathbf{b}$ and $\overrightarrow{AX} = 2\overrightarrow{OB}$.

  (a) Find, in terms of **a** and **b**,

     (i) $\overrightarrow{AX}$,      (ii) $\overrightarrow{BX}$.

  (b) $M$ and $N$ are the midpoints of $OA$ and $BX$ respectively.

     (i) Find $\overrightarrow{MN}$, in terms of **a** and **b**.
     (ii) What can you say about the lines $OB$ and $MN$?
     (iii) What type of quadrilateral is $OMNB$?

  (a) (i) $\overrightarrow{AX} = 2\mathbf{b}$     (ii) $\overrightarrow{BX} = \mathbf{a} + \mathbf{b}$

  (b) (i) $\overrightarrow{MN} = 1\frac{1}{2}\mathbf{b}$    (ii) $2\overrightarrow{MN} = 3\overrightarrow{OB}$    (iii) Trapezium
                            $MN$ is parallel to $OB$.

The diagrams in this exercise have not been drawn accurately.

**1** In the diagram, $\overrightarrow{OX} = \mathbf{x}$ and $\overrightarrow{OY} = \mathbf{y}$.

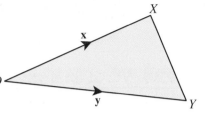

(a) Write, in terms of $\mathbf{x}$ and $\mathbf{y}$, the vector $\overrightarrow{XY}$.

(b) $P$ and $Q$ are the midpoints of $OX$ and $OY$ respectively.

Find, in terms of $\mathbf{x}$ and $\mathbf{y}$, the vector $\overrightarrow{QP}$.

**2** $A$ is the point $(2, 3)$ and $B$ is the point $(-2, 0)$.

(a) (i) Write $\overrightarrow{AB}$ as a column vector.

(ii) Find the length of the vector $\overrightarrow{AB}$.

$D$ is the point such that $\overrightarrow{BD}$ is parallel to $\binom{0}{1}$ and the length of $\overrightarrow{AD}$ = the length of $\overrightarrow{AB}$.
$O$ is the point $(0, 0)$.

(b) Find $\overrightarrow{OD}$ as a column vector.

$C$ is the point such that $ABCD$ is a rhombus.
$AC$ is a diagonal of the rhombus.
(c) Find the coordinates of $C$. Edexcel

**3** $PQRS$ is a parallelogram.
$T$ is the midpoint of $QR$.
$U$ is the point on $SR$ for which $SU : UR = 1 : 2$.
$\overrightarrow{PQ} = \mathbf{a}$ and $\overrightarrow{PS} = \mathbf{b}$.

Write down, in terms of $\mathbf{a}$ and $\mathbf{b}$, expressions for

(a) $\overrightarrow{PT}$, (b) $\overrightarrow{TU}$. Edexcel

**4** $A$ is the point $(1, 3)$ and $B$ is the point $(-3, 0)$.

(a) Find $\overrightarrow{AB}$ as a column vector.

$C$ is the point such that $\overrightarrow{BC} = \binom{4}{9}$.

(b) Write down the coordinates of the point $C$.

$X$ is the midpoint of $AB$.
$O$ is the origin.

(c) Find $\overrightarrow{OX}$ as a column vector. Edexcel

**5** The diagram shows a triangle $ABC$.
$P$ is the midpoint of $AB$
and $Q$ is the point on $AC$ such that $QC = 2AQ$.
$\overrightarrow{AP} = \mathbf{x}$ and $\overrightarrow{AQ} = \mathbf{y}$.

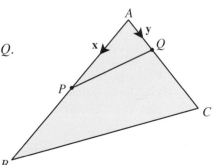

(a) Write $\overrightarrow{PQ}$ in terms of $\mathbf{x}$ and $\mathbf{y}$.

$T$ is a point such that $\overrightarrow{AT} = \overrightarrow{BC}$.
(b) Show that $PQT$ is a straight line. Edexcel

## What you need to know

● The graphs of the trigonometric functions.

The **sine function** is a periodic function with period 360°.
$-1 \leqslant \sin x \leqslant 1$

The **cosine function** is a periodic function with period 360°.
$-1 \leqslant \cos x \leqslant 1$

The **tangent function** is a periodic function with period 180°.
Tan $x$ is undefined at 90°, 270°, ...

● For every angle $x°$, the signs of $\sin x°$, $\cos x°$ and $\tan x°$ can be shown on a diagram.

> **Positive** angles are measured **anticlockwise**.
> **Negative** angles are measured **clockwise**.

For angles greater than 360°: subtract 360°, or multiples of 360°, to get the equivalent angle between 0° and 360°.

| | 90° | |
|---|---|---|
| **Sin** positive | | **All** positive |
| 180° | | 0° / 360° |
| **Tan** positive | | **Cos** positive |
| | 270° | |

**Eg 1**  Sin 53.1° = 0.8, correct to 1 d.p.
   (a)  Write down the other value of $x$ for which   $\sin x = 0.8$   for $0° \leqslant x \leqslant 360°$.
   (b)  Solve the equation   $\sin x = -0.8$   for $0° \leqslant x \leqslant 360°$.

(a)
> Always work from 0° or 180° or 360°.
> When $\sin x$ is positive:
> $\sin x = \sin (180° - x)$

$x = 180° - 53.1° = 126.9°$

(b)
> Sin $x$ is negative, so values of $x$ lie between 180° and 360°

$x = 180° + 53.1° = 233.1°$
$x = 360° - 53.1° = 306.9°$
So,   $x = 233.1°$   or   306.9°

● The **exact values** of the trigonometric ratios for the angles 30°, 45° and 60° can be found from the triangles below.

| | 30° | 45° | 60° |
|---|---|---|---|
| sin | $\frac{1}{2}$ | $\frac{1}{\sqrt{2}}$ | $\frac{\sqrt{3}}{2}$ |
| cos | $\frac{\sqrt{3}}{2}$ | $\frac{1}{\sqrt{2}}$ | $\frac{1}{2}$ |
| tan | $\frac{1}{\sqrt{3}}$ | 1 | $\sqrt{3}$ |

● You should be able to use the **sine rule** and the **cosine rule** to solve problems involving triangles which are not right-angled.

● **The Sine Rule**

$$\frac{a}{\sin A} = \frac{b}{\sin B} = \frac{c}{\sin C}$$

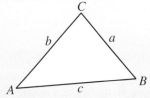

This can also be written as:   $\dfrac{\sin A}{a} = \dfrac{\sin B}{b} = \dfrac{\sin C}{c}$

**Eg 2** Calculate the length of side $a$.

$$\frac{a}{\sin 53°} = \frac{6}{\sin 47°}$$

$$a = \frac{6 \times \sin 53°}{\sin 47°}$$

$$a = 6.551...$$

$$a = 6.6 \text{ cm, to } 1 \text{ d.p.}$$

To find a **side** you need:
two angles of known size, **and** the length of a side which is opposite one of the known angles.

**Eg 3** Calculate the size of angle $P$.

$$\frac{\sin P}{9} = \frac{\sin 65°}{10}$$

$$\sin P = \frac{9 \times \sin 65°}{10}$$

$$\sin P = 0.8156...$$

$$P = 54.7°, \text{ to } 1 \text{ d.p.}$$

To find an **angle** you need:
the length of the side opposite the angle you are trying to find, **and** the length of a side opposite an angle of known size.

● **The Cosine Rule**

$$a^2 = b^2 + c^2 - 2bc \cos A$$

When using the Cosine Rule to find the size of an angle it is sometimes easier to rearrange the above formula as:

$$\cos A = \frac{b^2 + c^2 - a^2}{2bc}$$

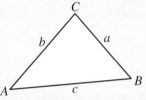

**Eg 4** Calculate the length of side $x$.

$$x^2 = 6^2 + 7^2 - 2 \times 6 \times 7 \times \cos 73°$$

$$x^2 = 36 + 49 - 24.55...$$

$$x^2 = 60.44...$$

$$x = 7.8 \text{ cm, to } 1 \text{ d.p.}$$

To find a **side** you need:
two sides of known length, **and** the size of the angle between the known sides.

**Eg 5** Calculate the size of angle $A$.

$$\cos A = \frac{6^2 + 8^2 - 7^2}{2 \times 6 \times 8}$$

$$\cos A = 0.53125$$

$$A = 57.9°, \text{ to } 1 \text{ d.p.}$$

To find an **angle** you need:
three sides of known length.

● You should be able to find the area of a triangle which is not right-angled.

**Eg 6** Calculate the area of triangle $PQR$.

$$\text{Area} = \frac{1}{2} \times 3 \times 7 \times \sin 108°$$

$$= 9.986...$$

$$= 10.0 \text{ cm}^2, \text{ to } 1 \text{ d.p.}$$

To find the **area of a triangle** you need:
two sides of known length, **and** the size of the angle between the known sides.

$$\text{Area} = \frac{1}{2} ab \sin C.$$

● You should be able to solve problems involving triangles.

For **right-angled triangles** use:
the **trigonometric ratios** (sin, cos and tan), **Pythagoras' Theorem**.

For **triangles which are not right-angled** use:
the **Sine Rule** or the **Cosine Rule**.

Do not use a calculator for questions 1 and 2.

**1** (a) $\cos 60° = 0.5$
  (i) Write down the other value of $x$ for which $\cos x = 0.5$ for $0° \leqslant x \leqslant 360°$.
  (ii) Solve the equation $\cos x = -0.5$ for $0° \leqslant x \leqslant 360°$.
 (b) (i) On the same diagram, sketch the graphs of $y = \cos x$ and $y = \sin x$
     for $0° \leqslant x \leqslant 360°$.
  (ii) Hence, solve the equation $\cos x = \sin x$ for $0° \leqslant x \leqslant 360°$.

**2** $\sin x° = \dfrac{\sqrt{3}}{2}$ and $0 < x < 90$.

 (a) Find the exact value of $\cos x°$.

 One value of $x$ for which $\sin x° = \dfrac{\sqrt{3}}{2}$ is 60.

 (b) Find two values of $y$ between 0 and 180 for which $\sin (2y)° = \dfrac{\sqrt{3}}{2}$.

Edexcel

**3**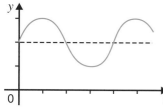

The depth of water in a harbour varies according to the formula $y = 10 + 5 \sin (30t)°$.
($y$ is the depth of the water in feet; $t$ is the time in hours.)
The sketch shows the graph of this formula.
 (a) Copy the graph and complete the labelling on the $t$ and $y$ axes.

A ship wishes to leave the harbour, but needs a depth of water of 13 feet to do so safely.
When the time is 1200 hours the value of $t$ is zero.
 (b) At what time can the ship first leave the harbour safely?

Edexcel

**4**

In the triangle $PQR$, angle $PQR = 108°$.
$PQ = 12.3$ cm and $PR = 24.4$ cm.

 (a) Calculate angle $QRP$.
 (b) Calculate the area of triangle $PQR$.

**5** The diagram shows a lighthouse, $L$, and two points, $A$ and $B$, on the sea.
$AL = 5$ km and $BL = 6$ km.
Angle $ALB = 150°$.

A boat sails in a straight line from point $A$ to point $B$.
 (a) Calculate the distance $AB$.

At its shortest distance from the lighthouse,
the boat is at the point $X$ on the line $AB$.
 (b) Calculate the distance $LX$.

Edexcel

**6**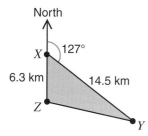

The diagram shows the positions of ships $X$, $Y$ and $Z$.
$X$ is 6.3 km due North of $Z$.
$Y$ is 14.5 km from $X$ on a bearing of 127°.

Calculate the distance and bearing of $Z$ from $Y$.

**7** In the triangle $ABC$, $AB = 6$ cm and $AC = 9$ cm.
The area of triangle $ABC$ is 24 cm².
 (a) Calculate the two possible values of angle $BAC$.
 (b) Calculate the length of $BC$, when angle $BAC$ is obtuse.

Do not use a calculator for this exercise.

**1** (a) Draw a square, a rhombus and a kite. Mark equal sides, parallel sides and equal angles.
(b) Which quadrilaterals have four equal angles?
(c) A rhombus is a special type of parallelogram as it possesses **all** the properties of a parallelogram. Which other special types of quadrilateral can a rhombus be?  Edexcel

**2** This dial shows how much petrol is in the petrol tank of a car.
The full petrol tank holds 40 litres.
Estimate how many litres of petrol are in the petrol tank.

Edexcel

**3** Work out the area of each shape.

(a)

3 cm
12 cm

(b)

8 cm
2 cm
5 cm
3 cm

**4** (a) Work out the size of an exterior angle of a regular pentagon.

The area of a pentagon is 8560 mm².
(b) Change 8560 mm² to cm².  Edexcel

**5** $AC = BC$.
$AB$ is parallel to $DC$.  Angle $ABC = 52°$.

(a) Work out the value of  (i) $p$,   (ii) $q$.

The angles marked $p°$ and $r°$ are equal.
(b) What geometrical name is given to this type of equal angles?

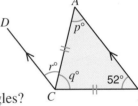

Edexcel

**6** Work out the bearing of

(a) $B$ from $P$,

(b) $P$ from $A$.

North
63°
138°
A
P
B

Edexcel

**7** Copy the diagram onto squared paper.
(a) $P$ is mapped onto $Q$ by an enlargement, scale factor 2, centre $(-1, 3)$. Draw and label $Q$.
(b) $P$ is mapped onto $R$ by a translation with vector $\begin{pmatrix} -3 \\ 2 \end{pmatrix}$. Draw and label $R$.
(c) Describe the single transformation which maps $Q$ onto $R$.

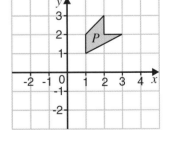

**8** A circle has an area of $49\pi$ cm².
Calculate the circumference of the circle in terms of $\pi$.

**9** (a) Construct triangle $ABC$, in which  $AB = 9.5$ cm,  $BC = 8$ cm  and  $CA = 6$ cm.
(b) Using ruler and compasses only,
(i) bisect angle $BAC$,
(ii) draw the locus of points that are equidistant from $A$ and $C$.
(c) Shade the region inside the triangle where all the points are less than 7.5 cm from $B$, nearer to $A$ than to $C$ and nearer to $AC$ than to $AB$.

**10** (a) Calculate the sum of the interior angles of a regular 10-sided polygon.

(b) The diagram shows a square and a regular hexagon which meet at $M$.
$LM$ and $MN$ are two sides of another regular polygon.
How many sides has this polygon?

**11** The following formulae represent certain quantities connected with containers, where $a$, $b$ and $c$ are dimensions.

$$\pi a \qquad abc \qquad \sqrt{a^2 - c^2} \qquad \pi a^2 b \qquad 2(a + b + c)$$

(a) Explain why $abc$ represents a volume.

(b) Which of these formulae represent lengths?

**12** Simone made a scale model of a "hot rod" car on a scale of 1 to 12.5.
The height of the model car is 10 cm.

(a) Work out the height of the real car.

The length of the real car is 5 m.

(b) Work out the length of the model car. Give your answer in centimetres.

The angle the windscreen makes with the bonnet on the real car is 140°.

(c) What is the angle the windscreen makes with the bonnet on the model car?

The width of the windscreen in the real car is 119 cm, correct to the nearest centimetre.

(d) Write down the smallest length this measurement could be.

Edexcel

**13**

The diagram shows a wedge in the shape of a triangular prism.
The cross-section of the prism is shown as a shaded triangle.
The area of the triangle is 15 cm².
The length of the prism is 10 cm.
Work out the volume of the prism.

Edexcel

**14** A rectangular painting which measures 40 cm by 25 cm fits into a rectangular frame which measures 50 cm by 35 cm.

Show that the two rectangles are not similar.

**15**

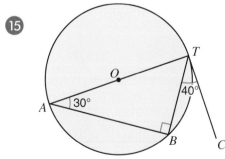

$T$, $A$ and $B$ are points on the circumference of the circle, centre $O$.
$AT$ is a diameter of the circle.
Angle $BTC = 40°$.
Angle $TAB = 30°$.

Explain why $TC$ cannot be a tangent to the circle.

Edexcel

**16** Tan $XYZ = \frac{4}{3}$.

(a) Find (i) sin $XYZ$, (ii) cos $XYZ$.

(b) When $XZ = 10$ cm, what are the lengths of $XY$ and $YZ$?

**17**

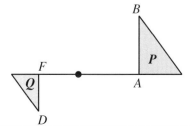

Triangle $P$ is mapped to triangle $Q$ by an enlargement of scale factor $-0.5$.
If $AB$ is of length 6.4 cm, how long is $FD$?

Edexcel

**18**

The diagram represents a large cone of height 6 cm and base diameter 18 cm.
The large cone is made by placing a small cone, *A*, of height 2 cm and base diameter 6 cm, on top of a frustum, *B*.

Calculate the volume of the frustum, *B*.
Give your answer in terms of $\pi$.

Edexcel

**19** A hemispherical bowl has a diameter of 18 cm.

Calculate the volume of the bowl.
Give your answer in terms of $\pi$.

**20** Sketch the graphs of $y = \sin x°$ and $y = \cos 2x°$ for $0° \leqslant x \leqslant 360°$.
Hence, find all the solutions of the equation $\sin x° = \cos 2x°$ for $0° \leqslant x \leqslant 360°$.

**21**

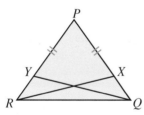

Triangle *PQR* is isosceles with *PQ* = *PR*.

*X* is a point on *PQ*.
*Y* is a point on *PR*.
*PX* = *PY*.

Prove that triangle *PQY* is congruent to triangle *PRX*.

Edexcel

**22** The diagram shows two triangles, *OAB* and *OCD*.
*OAC* and *OBD* are straight lines.
*AB* is parallel to *CD*.

$\overrightarrow{OA} = \mathbf{a}$ and $\overrightarrow{OB} = \mathbf{b}$.

The point *A* cuts the line *OC* in the ratio *OA* : *OC* = 2 : 3.

Express $\overrightarrow{CD}$ in terms of **a** and **b**.

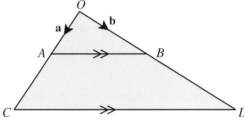

Edexcel

**23** *A*, *B*, *C*, and *D* are points on the circumference of a circle centre *O*.

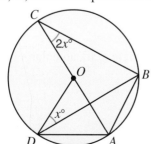

*AC* is a diameter of the circle.
Angle *BDO* = $x°$.
Angle *BCA* = $2x°$.

Express, in terms of *x*, the size of
(a) angle *BDA*,
(b) angle *AOD*,
(c) angle *ABD*.

Edexcel

# Shape, Space and Measures Calculator Paper

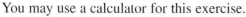

You may use a calculator for this exercise.

**1** Colin is 5 feet 10 inches tall and weighs 11 stones.
On a medical form he is asked to give his height in centimetres and his weight in kilograms.
What values should he give?

**2** (a) Copy the diagram.
Shade **one** square so that the shape has exactly **one** line of symmetry.
(b) Make **another** copy of the diagram.
Shade **one** square so that the shape has rotational symmetry of order 2.

Edexcel

**3** The radius of a circle is 6.4 cm.
Work out the circumference of this circle.

Edexcel

**4** The diagram shows a square-based pyramid.
(a) How many planes of symmetry has the pyramid?
(b) How many axes of symmetry has the pyramid?

**5**

The diagram shows the plan of a swimming pool.
The arc *QR* is a semi-circle.
*PS* = 12 m   and   *PQ* = *RS* = 20 m.

Calculate the area of the surface of the pool.

**6** The distance of a helicopter from the radio mast is 70 km, correct to the nearest kilometre.
Write down
(a) the maximum distance the helicopter could be from the radio mast,
(b) the minimum distance the helicopter could be from the radio mast.

Edexcel

**7** The diagram shows the angle formed when three regular polygons
are placed together, as shown.

(a) Explain why angle *a* is 120°.
(b) Work out the size of the angle marked *b*.

**8**

A can of drink is in the shape of a cylinder.
The can has a radius of 4 cm and a height of 15 cm.

Calculate the volume of the cylinder.

Edexcel

**9** A skip is in the shape of a prism with cross-section *ABCD*.
*AD* = 2.3 m,   *DC* = 1.3 m   and   *BC* = 1.7 m.
The width of the skip is 1.5 m.

(a) Calculate the area of the shape *ABCD*.
(b) Calculate the volume of the skip.

Edexcel

**10** Plot the points $P(1, 4)$ and $Q(6, 2)$.
Construct accurately the locus of all points which are equidistant from $P$ and $Q$. Edexcel

**11** Three oil rigs, $X$, $Y$ and $Z$, are supplied by boats from port $P$.
$X$ is 15 km from $P$ on a bearing of $050°$. $Y$ is 20 km from $P$ on a bearing of $110°$.
$Z$ is equidistant from $X$ and $Y$ and 30 km from $P$.
(a) By using a scale of 1 cm to represent 5 km, draw an accurate diagram to show the positions of $P$, $X$, $Y$ and $Z$.
(b) Use your diagram to find
  (i) the bearing of $Y$ from $Z$, (ii) the distance, in kilometres, of $Y$ from $Z$.

**12** Triangle $PQR$ is drawn on the grid.
The point $S$ is also shown.

Copy triangle $PQR$ onto squared paper and enlarge the triangle $PQR$ using a scale factor of $\frac{1}{2}$.
Use $S$ as the centre of enlargement.

Edexcel

**13**

The diagram shows Fay's house, $H$, and her school, $S$.
To get to school Fay has a choice of two routes.
She can either walk along Waverly Crescent or along the footpaths $HX$ and $XS$.
Waverly Crescent is a semi-circle with diameter 650 m.
The footpath $HX$ is 250 m and meets the footpath $XS$ at right-angles.
Which of these routes is shorter? By how much?

**14** $BE$ is parallel to $CD$.
$ABC$ and $AED$ are straight lines.
$AB = 6$ cm, $BC = 24$ cm,
$CD = 20$ cm, $AE = 3$ cm.
(a) Calculate the length of $BE$.
(b) Calculate the length of $DE$.

Edexcel

**15**
Ballymena is due West of Larne.
Woodburn is 15 km due South of Larne.
Ballymena is 32 km from Woodburn.
Calculate the distance of Larne from Ballymena.

**16** $O$ is the centre of a circle through $P$, $Q$, $R$ and $S$.
(a) Work out the size of angle $QRS$.
(b) $X$ is a point on the minor arc $PS$.
  Explain why angle $PXS = 140°$.

**17**

A cylindrical can has a radius of 6 centimetres.
The capacity of the can is 2000 cm³.
Calculate the height of the can.
Give your answer correct to 1 decimal place.

Edexcel

**18** When Jessie is standing 12 m from the bottom of a flag pole she finds the angle of elevation to the top of the pole is $37°$. Calculate the height of the flag pole.

**19** Find the two values of $x$ between $0°$ and $360°$ which satisfy the equation $4 \cos x = -1$.

**20** Three points, $A$, $B$ and $C$, on horizontal ground are such that
$AB = 10$ m and $\cos \angle ABC = 0.6$.
The point $P$ lies on $BC$ and $\angle APB = 90°$.
A vertical pole, $VA$, of height 19 m is placed at $A$.

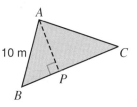

Calculate the angle between　(a)　$VB$ and the horizontal,
　　　　　　　　　　　　　　　(b)　$VP$ and the horizontal.

Edexcel

**21**

The diagram shows two concentric circles with centre $O$.
$\angle XOY = 118°$. $OX = 8.5$ cm.

(a) Calculate the area of the sector $XOY$.

(b) The arc $AB = 5$ cm.
Calculate $OA$.

**22** In the diagram $\overrightarrow{OA} = \mathbf{a}$ and $\overrightarrow{OB} = \mathbf{b}$.
$B$ is the midpoint of $OX$.

(a) Find, in terms of $\mathbf{a}$ and $\mathbf{b}$, the vectors $\overrightarrow{OX}$ and $\overrightarrow{AX}$.

(b) $M$ is the midpoint of $AX$.
Prove that $BM$ is parallel to $OA$.

**23**

The area of triangle $ABC$ is $10$ cm$^2$.
$AB = 3.2$ cm. $BC = 8.4$ cm.

Calculate the perimeter of triangle $ABC$.

Edexcel

**24** In the quadrilateral $ABCD$,
$AB = 6$ cm, $BC = 7$ cm, $AD = 12$ cm,
angle $ABC = 120°$, angle $ACD = 70°$.
Calculate the size of angle $ADC$.

Edexcel

**25**

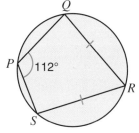

$PQRS$ is a cyclic quadrilateral in which:
$QR = RS$, $PS = 5.2$ cm and $PQ = 6.8$ cm.
$\angle SPQ = 112°$.

Calculate the length of $QR$.

**26** The stand on which the dog is sitting is the frustum of a cone.
The top of the stand has a radius of $0.5$ m.
The bottom of the stand has a radius of $1$ m.
The height of the stand is $0.6$ m.
(a) Calculate the volume of the stand.
(b) The height of a similar stand is $0.4$ m.
Calculate the volume of this stand.

**27** George constructs a triangle, $PQR$.
$PQ = 8.5$ cm and $QR = 5.1$ cm, correct to the nearest millimetre.
$\angle PQR = 118°$, correct to the nearest degree.
(a) Calculate the upper bound of the side $PR$.
(b) Calculate the lower bound for the area of triangle $PQR$.

# Collection and Organisation of Data

## What you need to know

- **Primary data** is data collected by an individual or organisation to use for a particular purpose. Primary data is obtained from experiments, investigations, surveys and by using questionnaires.

- **Secondary data** is data which is already available or has been collected by someone else for a different purpose. Sources of secondary data include the Annual Abstract of Statistics, Social Trends and the Internet.

- **Qualitative** data – Data which can only be described in words. E.g. Colour of cars.

- **Quantitative** data – Data that has a numerical value.
  Quantitative data is either **discrete** or **continuous**.
  **Discrete** data can only take certain values. E.g. Numbers of cars in car parks.
  **Continuous** data has no exact value and is measurable. E.g. Weights of cars.

- **Data Collection Sheets** – Used to record data during a survey.

- **Tally** – A way of recording each item of data on a data collection sheet.

- **Frequency Table** – A way of collating the information recorded on a data collection sheet.

- **Grouped Frequency Table** – Used for continuous data or for discrete data when a lot of data has to be recorded.

- **Database** – A collection of data.

- **Class Interval** – The width of the groups used in a grouped frequency distribution.

- **Questionnaire** – A set of questions used to collect data for a survey.
  Questionnaires should: (1) use simple language,
  (2) ask short questions which can be answered precisely,
  (3) provide tick boxes,
  (4) avoid open-ended questions,
  (5) avoid leading questions,
  (6) ask questions in a logical order.

- **Hypothesis** – A hypothesis is a statement which may or may not be true.

- When information is required about a large group of people it is not always possible to survey everyone and only a **sample** may be asked.
  The sample chosen should be large enough to make the results meaningful and representative of the whole group (population) or the results may be **biased**.

- **Two-way Tables** – A way of illustrating two features of a survey.

- In a **simple random sample** everyone has an equal chance of being selected.

- In a **systematic random sample** people are selected according to some rule.

- In a **stratified random sample** the original group is divided up into separate categories or strata, such as male/female, age group, etc, before a random sample is taken. A simple random sample is then taken from each category in proportion to the size of the category.

## Exercise 35

1. To find out how long students spend on homework each night, Pat asks a class of Year 7 students how much time they spent on their homework last night.
   Give two reasons why his results may not be typical of all students.

**2** Jamie is investigating the use made of his college library. Here is part of his questionnaire:

> **Library Questionnaire**
> 1. How old are you? ........................

(a) (i) Give a reason why this question is unsuitable.
   (ii) Rewrite the question so that it could be included.
(b) Jamie asks the librarian to give the questionnaires to students when they borrow books.
   (i) Give reasons why this sample may be biased.
   (ii) Suggest a better way of giving out the questionnaires.

**3** Martin, the local Youth Centre leader, wishes to know why attendance at the Youth Centre is less than at the same time last year. He thinks that it could be due to a number of changes that occurred during the course of the year. These changes were:

> **the opening hours changed,**
>
> **a new sports centre opened nearby,**
>
> **some of the older members started bullying the younger members.**

Design a suitable question, that is easily answered, to find out why people do not attend the Youth Centre.

*Edexcel*

**4** The table shows the results of a survey of 500 people.

|  | Can drive | Cannot drive |
|---|---|---|
| Men | 180 | 20 |
| Women | 240 | 60 |

A newspaper headline states: **Survey shows that more women can drive than men.**
Do the results of the survey support this headline? Give a reason for your answer.

**5** Explain briefly in what circumstances a stratified random sample might be taken rather than a simple random sample.

**6** There are 1000 students in Nigel and Sonia's school.
Nigel is carrying out a survey of the types of food eaten at lunchtime.
(a) Explain how Nigel could take a random sample of students to carry out this survey.

This table shows the gender and the number of students in each year group.

| Year group | 7 | 8 | 9 | 10 | 11 |
|---|---|---|---|---|---|
| Number of boys | 100 | 90 | 120 | 80 | 100 |
| Number of girls | 100 | 80 | 110 | 120 | 100 |
| Total | 200 | 170 | 230 | 200 | 200 |

Sonia is carrying out a survey about how much homework students are given.
She decides to take a stratified sample of 100 students from the whole school.
(b) Calculate how many in the stratified sample should be
   (i) students from Year 9, (ii) boys from Year 10.

*Edexcel*

**7** There are three secondary schools in a large town.
The number of pupils in each school is given in the table.

| Albert High School | 570 |
|---|---|
| St Joseph's High School | 965 |
| London Road School | 1015 |

A researcher wishes to find out what secondary school pupils feel about the standard of education in the town.
She chooses a representative sample of total size 50.
How many pupils should be chosen from each school?

*Edexcel*

Collection and Organisation of Data

## What you need to know

- There are three types of **average**: the **mode**, the **median** and the **mean**.
  The **mode** is the most common value.
  The **median** is the middle value (or the mean of the two middle values) when the values are arranged in order of size.

  The **Mean** = $\dfrac{\text{Total of all values}}{\text{Number of values}}$

- The **range** is a measure of **spread**, and is the difference between the highest and lowest values.

  **Eg 1**  The number of text messages received by 7 students on Saturday is shown.

  $$2 \quad 4 \quad 3 \quad 4 \quad 4 \quad 3 \quad 2$$

  Find   (a)  the mode,   (b)  the median,   (c)  the mean,   (d)  the range.

  (a)  The mode is 4.

  (b)  2   2   3   ③   4   4   4     The median is 3.

  (c)  The mean = $\dfrac{2 + 4 + 3 + 4 + 4 + 3 + 2}{7} = \dfrac{22}{7} = 3.14\ldots = 3.1$, correct to 1 d.p.

  (d)  The range = $4 - 2 = 2$

- To find the mean of a **frequency distribution** use:   Mean = $\dfrac{\text{Total of all values}}{\text{Number of values}} = \dfrac{\Sigma fx}{\Sigma f}$

  **Eg 2**  The table shows the number of stamps on some parcels.

  | Number of stamps | 1 | 2 | 3 | 4 |
  |---|---|---|---|---|
  | Number of parcels | 5 | 6 | 9 | 4 |

  Find the mean number of stamps per parcel.

  Mean = $\dfrac{\text{Total number of stamps}}{\text{Number of parcels}} = \dfrac{1 \times 5 + 2 \times 6 + 3 \times 9 + 4 \times 4}{5 + 6 + 9 + 4} = \dfrac{60}{24} = 2.5$

- To find the mean of a **grouped frequency distribution**, first find the value of the midpoint of each class.
  Then use:           Estimated mean = $\dfrac{\text{Total of all values}}{\text{Number of values}} = \dfrac{\Sigma fx}{\Sigma f}$

  **Eg 3**  The table shows the weights of some parcels.

  | Weight ($w$ grams) | Frequency |
  |---|---|
  | $100 \leqslant w < 200$ | 7 |
  | $200 \leqslant w < 300$ | 11 |
  | $300 \leqslant w < 400$ | 19 |
  | $400 \leqslant w < 500$ | 3 |

  Calculate an estimate of the mean weight of these parcels.

  Mean = $\dfrac{\Sigma fx}{\Sigma f} = \dfrac{150 \times 7 + 250 \times 11 + 350 \times 19 + 450 \times 3}{7 + 11 + 19 + 3} = \dfrac{11\,800}{40} = 295$ grams

- You should be able to choose the best average to use in different situations for different sets of data.

**1** The prices paid for eight different meals at a restaurant are:

£10     £9     £9.50     £12     £20     £11.50     £11     £9

(a) Which price is the mode?
(b) Find the median price.
(c) Calculate the mean price.
(d) Which of these averages best describes the average price paid for a meal?
     Give a reason for your answer.

**2** Some students took a mental arithmetic test.
Information about their marks is shown in the table.

| Mark | 4 | 5 | 6 | 7 | 8 | 9 | 10 |
|---|---|---|---|---|---|---|---|
| Frequency | 2 | 1 | 2 | 4 | 7 | 10 | 3 |

(a) Work out how many students took the test.
(b) Write down the modal mark.

24 students had a higher mark than Caroline.
(c) Work out Caroline's mark.
(d) Find the median mark.
(e) Work out the range of the marks.          Edexcel

**3** 75 boys took part in a darts competition.
Each boy threw darts until he hit the centre of the dartboard.
The numbers of darts thrown by the boys are grouped in this frequency table.

| Number of darts thrown | Frequency |
|---|---|
| 1 to 5 | 10 |
| 6 to 10 | 17 |
| 11 to 15 | 12 |
| 16 to 20 | 4 |
| 21 to 25 | 12 |
| 26 to 30 | 20 |

(a) Work out the class interval which contains the median.
(b) Work out an estimate for the mean number of darts thrown by each boy.          Edexcel

**4** The table shows the number of students in three groups attending Maths City High School
last Monday. No student belonged to more than one group.

| Group | A | B | C |
|---|---|---|---|
| Number of students | 135 | 225 | 200 |

Mrs Allen carried out a survey about the students' travelling times from home to school
last Monday. Mrs Allen worked out that:
● the mean time for Group A students was 24 minutes,
● the mean time for Group B students was 32 minutes,
● the mean time for Group C students was the same as the mean time for all 560 students.
Work out the mean time for all 560 students.          Edexcel

**5** A survey was carried out to find out how much time was needed by a group of pupils to
complete homework set on a particular Monday evening. The results are shown in the table.

| Time ($t$ hours) spent on homework | 0 | $0 < t \leqslant 1$ | $1 < t \leqslant 2$ | $2 < t \leqslant 3$ | $3 < t \leqslant 4$ |
|---|---|---|---|---|---|
| Number of pupils | 3 | 14 | 17 | 5 | 1 |

Calculate an estimate for the mean time spent on homework by the pupils in the group. Edexcel

Averages and Range

## What you need to know

- **Bar chart**. Used for data which can be counted.
  Often used to compare quantities of data in a distribution.
  The length of each bar represents frequency.

  > Bars can be drawn horizontally or vertically.

- **Bar-line graph**. Instead of drawing bars, horizontal or vertical lines are drawn to show frequency.

- **Pie chart**. Used for data which can be counted.
  Often used to compare proportions of data, usually with the total.
  The whole circle represents all the data.
  The size of each sector represents the frequency of data in that sector.

  **Eg 1** The results of asking a group of children which board game they liked best is shown.

  | Board game | Chess | Draughts | Ludo | Snakes & Ladders |
  |---|---|---|---|---|
  | Number of children | 4 | 9 | 2 | 5 |

  Draw a pie chart to show this information.
  20 children were asked.
  Each child is represented by $\frac{360°}{20} = 18°$.

  Chess: $4 \times 18° = 72°$
  Draughts: $9 \times 18° = 162°$
  Ludo: $2 \times 18° = 36°$
  Snakes & Ladders: $5 \times 18° = 90°$

- **Stem and leaf diagrams**. Used to represent data in its original form.
  Data is split into two parts.
  The part with the higher place value is the stem.     E.g.   15 = stem 1, leaf 5.
  A key is given to show the value of the data.     E.g.   3|4 means 3.4, etc.
  The data is shown in numerical order on the diagram.     E.g.   2|3 5 9 represents 23, 25, 29.
  **Back to back stem and leaf diagrams** can be used to compare two sets of data.

  **Eg 2** The times, in seconds, taken by 10 students to complete a puzzle are shown.
  
  $$9 \quad 23 \quad 17 \quad 20 \quad 12 \quad 11 \quad 24 \quad 12 \quad 10 \quad 26$$
  
  Construct a stem and leaf diagram to represent this information.

  2 | 0   means 20 seconds

  | 0 | 9 | | | | |
  |---|---|---|---|---|---|
  | 1 | 0 | 1 | 2 | 2 | 7 |
  | 2 | 0 | 3 | 4 | 6 | |

- A **scatter graph** can be used to show the relationship between two sets of data.

- The relationship between two sets of data is referred to as **correlation**.

- You should be able to recognise **positive** and **negative** correlation.
  The correlation is stronger as points get closer to a straight line.

- When there is a relationship between two sets of data a **line of best fit** can be drawn on the scatter graph.

- **Perfect correlation** is when all the points lie on a straight line.

- The line of best fit can be used to **estimate** the value from one set of the data when the corresponding value of the other set is known.

Positive correlation     Negative correlation

**Eg 3** The table shows the weights and heights of 10 girls.

| Weight (kg) | 33 | 36 | 37 | 39 | 40 | 42 | 45 | 45 | 48 | 48 |
|---|---|---|---|---|---|---|---|---|---|---|
| Height (cm) | 133 | 134 | 137 | 140 | 146 | 146 | 145 | 150 | 152 | 156 |

(a) Draw a scatter graph for the data.
(b) What type of correlation is shown?
(c) Draw a line of best fit.
(d) A girl weighs 50 kg. Estimate her height.

> Mark a cross on the graph to show the weight and height of each girl.

(a)

> **On a scatter graph:**
> The **slope** of the line of best fit shows the **trend** of the data.
> The line of best fit does not have to go through the origin of the graph.

(b) Positive correlation.
(c) The line of best fit has been drawn, by eye, on the graph.
(d) 158 cm. Read estimate where 50 kg meets line of best fit.

## Exercise 37

**1** Here are the highest November temperatures recorded in 12 European countries last year.

  13°C  9°C  14°C  17°C  14°C  20°C  7°C  14°C  18°C  21°C  10°C  22°C

(a) Construct a stem and leaf diagram to show this information.
(b) When the temperature in another European country is included in the data, the range increases by 2°C.
What was the temperature recorded in that country? Explain your answer.

**2** 40 passengers at Gatwick Airport were asked which country they were flying to.
Here is a frequency table which shows that information.

| Country | USA | France | Spain | Greece |
|---|---|---|---|---|
| Number of passengers | 14 | 10 | 11 | 5 |

Draw an accurate pie chart to show this information.                    Edexcel

**3** The scatter graphs show the results of a survey given to people on holiday at a seaside resort.

(a) Which scatter graph shows the temperature (°C) plotted against:
  (i) the number of people in the sea,
  (ii) the number of people with coats on,
  (iii) the amount of money people spend?
(b) Which scatter graph shows a positive correlation?

**4** The bar chart shows information about the injuries of drivers involved in road accidents at a busy junction.

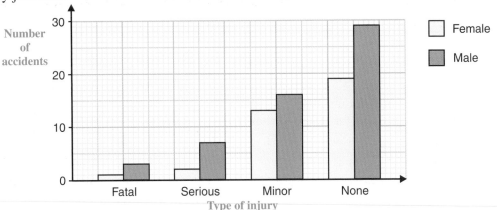

(a) What percentage of drivers had no injuries?
(b) Find, in its simple form, the ratio of female to male drivers involved in these accidents.
(c) Draw a pie chart to illustrate the proportion of drivers with each type of injury.

**5** The pie chart gives information about the bills paid by a Water Company.

(a) Work out the size of the angle representing Wages.

The Water Company spent £18 000 on Materials.
(b) Work out the amount it spent on Rates.

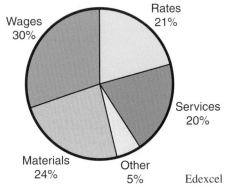

Edexcel

**6** Twenty children were asked to estimate the length of a leaf.
Their estimates, in centimetres, are:

| **Boys** | | | | |
|---|---|---|---|---|
| 4.5 | 5.0 | 4.0 | 3.5 | 4.0 |
| 4.5 | 5.0 | 4.5 | 3.5 | 4.5 |

| **Girls** | | | | |
|---|---|---|---|---|
| 4.5 | 5.0 | 3.5 | 4.0 | 5.5 |
| 3.5 | 4.5 | 3.5 | 3.0 | 2.5 |

(a) Construct a back to back stem and leaf diagram to represent this information.
(b) Compare and comment on the estimates of these boys and girls.

**7** On seven days, Helen recorded the time, in minutes, it took a 2 cm ice cube to melt.
She also recorded the temperature, in °C, on that day.
All of her results are shown in the table below.

| Temperature (°C) | 9 | 11.5 | 15 | 17 | 20 | 21 | 26 |
|---|---|---|---|---|---|---|---|
| Time (minutes) | 63 | 55 | 48 | 40 | 30 | 25 | 12.5 |

(a) Draw a scatter graph for the data.
(b) Describe the relationship between the temperature and the time it takes a 2 cm ice cube to melt.
(c) Draw a line of best fit on your scatter graph.
(d) Use your line of best fit to estimate the time it took for a 2 cm ice cube to melt when the temperature was 13°C.
(e) Use your line of best fit to estimate the temperature when a 2 cm ice cube took 19 minutes to melt.
(f) Explain why the line of best fit could not be used to estimate the time it took a 2 cm ice cube to melt when the temperature was 35°C.

Edexcel

# Presentation of Data 2

## What you need to know

- A **time series** is a set of readings taken at time intervals.

- A **line graph** is used to show a time series.

> Only the plotted points represent actual values. Points are joined by lines to show the **trend**.

- Variations in a time series which recur with the seasons of the year are called **seasonal variations**.

- **Moving averages** are used to smooth out variations in a time series so that the trend can be seen.

**Eg 1** The graph shows the amount of gas used by a householder each quarter over a period of 3 years.

The blue crosses show the 4-quarterly moving average values.

A line of best fit, drawn for the moving averages, shows the general **trend**.

The trend shows a slight increase in the amount of gas used.

- **Frequency polygon**. Used to illustrate grouped frequency distributions. Often used to compare two or more distributions on the same diagram.

**Eg 2** The frequency distribution of the heights of some boys is shown.

| Height ($h$ cm) | $130 \leqslant h < 140$ | $140 \leqslant h < 150$ | $150 \leqslant h < 160$ | $160 \leqslant h < 170$ | $170 \leqslant h < 180$ |
|---|---|---|---|---|---|
| Frequency | 1 | 7 | 12 | 9 | 3 |

Draw a frequency polygon to illustrate the data.

> Frequencies are plotted at the midpoints of the class intervals and joined with straight lines.

- **Histograms**. Used to illustrate grouped frequency distributions.
  The horizontal axis is a continuous scale.
  Bars are drawn between the lower and upper class boundaries for each class interval.
  When the classes have gaps between them the upper class boundary is halfway between the end of one class and the beginning of the next.

- Histograms can have equal or unequal class width intervals.
  With **equal** class width intervals:   **frequency** is proportional to the **heights** of the bars.
  With **unequal** class width intervals:   **frequency** is proportional to the **areas** of the bars.

> frequency = frequency density × class width interval

**Eg 3** The times taken by 40 pupils to solve a puzzle are:

| Time ($t$ seconds) | $10 \leqslant t < 20$ | $20 \leqslant t < 25$ | $25 \leqslant t < 30$ | $30 \leqslant t < 45$ |
|---|---|---|---|---|
| Frequency | 6 | 12 | 10 | 12 |

Draw a histogram to represent the data.

**To find the height of each bar:**
The height of each bar is given by the **frequency density** for each group, where:

$$\text{frequency density} = \frac{\text{frequency}}{\text{class width interval}}$$

E.g. For the group $10 \leqslant t < 20$:  Frequency density $\frac{6}{10} = 0.6$
Draw the bar to a height of 0.6

## Exercise 38

**1**   The table shows the number of units of electricity used each quarter by a householder over a period of 3 years.

| Year | 2003 | | | | 2004 | | | | 2005 | | | |
|---|---|---|---|---|---|---|---|---|---|---|---|---|
| Quarter | 1 | 2 | 3 | 4 | 1 | 2 | 3 | 4 | 1 | 2 | 3 | 4 |
| Units used | 680 | 810 | 470 | 740 | 640 | 850 | 420 | 750 | 970 | 880 | 490 | 760 |

(a)   Plot these values on graph paper.
(b)   Calculate a 4-point moving average.
(c)   Plot the moving average values on your graph.
(d)   Comment on the trend in the units of electricity used.

**2**   The table shows the frequency distribution of student absences for a year.

| Absences ($d$ days) | Frequency |
|---|---|
| $0 < d < 5$ | 4 |
| $5 \leqslant d < 10$ | 6 |
| $10 \leqslant d < 15$ | 8 |
| $15 \leqslant d < 20$ | 5 |
| $20 \leqslant d < 25$ | 4 |
| $25 \leqslant d < 30$ | 3 |

(a)   Draw a frequency polygon for this frequency distribution.
(b)   Write down the class which contains the median.

Edexcel

**3** The graph shows the age distribution of people in a nursing home.

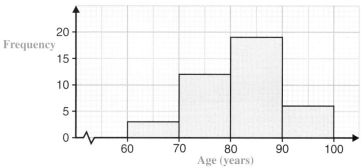

(a) Which age group is the modal class?

(b) How many people are in the nursing home?

(c) The table shows the age distribution of men in the home.

| Age ($a$ years) | $60 \leq a < 70$ | $70 \leq a < 80$ | $80 \leq a < 90$ | $90 \leq a < 100$ |
|---|---|---|---|---|
| Frequency | 2 | 7 | 6 | 0 |

  (i) Draw a frequency polygon to represent this information.

  (ii) On the same diagram draw a frequency polygon to represent the age distribution of women in the home.

  (iii) Compare and comment on the ages of men and women in the home.

**4** Kim sowed some seeds in her greenhouse.

10 weeks later she measured the heights of the plants.

Some of the results are shown in the table and the histogram.

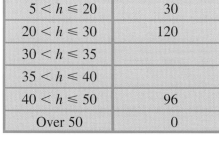

| Height ($h$) in cm | Number of plants |
|---|---|
| $0 < h \leq 5$ | 0 |
| $5 < h \leq 20$ | 30 |
| $20 < h \leq 30$ | 120 |
| $30 < h \leq 35$ | |
| $35 < h \leq 40$ | |
| $40 < h \leq 50$ | 96 |
| Over 50 | 0 |

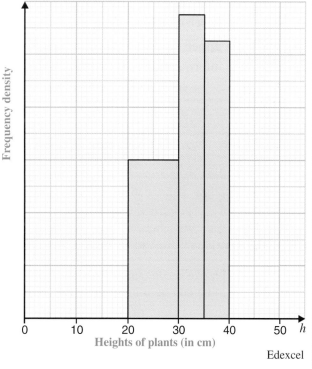

(a) Copy and complete the table and the histogram.

Kim had sown 500 seeds.

(b) Calculate the number of seeds that had not produced plants.

Edexcel

**5** The weights of some babies are given in the table.

| Weight ($W$ kg) | $0 \leq W < 2$ | $2 \leq W < 2.5$ | $2.5 \leq W < 3$ | $3 \leq W < 4$ | $4 \leq W < 6$ | $W \geq 6$ |
|---|---|---|---|---|---|---|
| Frequency | 0 | 8 | 9 | 15 | 27 | 0 |

Draw a histogram to show the distribution of weights of the babies.

Use a scale of 2 cm to 1 kg on the weight axis.

Edexcel

# Cumulative Frequency

## What you need to know

- The information given in a frequency table can be used to make a **cumulative frequency table**.
- You should be able to **draw cumulative frequency graphs**.

> **To draw a cumulative frequency graph:**
> 1. Draw and label:
>    the variable on the horizontal axis,
>    cumulative frequency on the vertical axis.
> 2. Plot the cumulative frequency against the
>    upper class boundary of each class.
> 3. Join the points with a smooth curve.

- If the question does not give the upper class boundaries,
  then the upper class boundary of each class is equal to the lower class boundary of the next class.
- When the classes have gaps between them then the upper class boundary is halfway between the
  end of one class and the beginning of the next.
- You should be able to **interpret cumulative frequency graphs**.

> The **median** is the value of the middle number.
>
> The **lower quartile** is the value located at $\frac{1}{4}$ of the total frequency.
>
> The **upper quartile** is the value located at $\frac{3}{4}$ of the total frequency.
>
> The **interquartile range** measures the spread of the middle 50% of the data.
> $$\text{Interquartile range} = \text{Upper Quartile} - \text{Lower Quartile}$$

**Eg 1** The times spent by students on the Internet one day are shown.

| Time ($t$ minutes) | $0 \leqslant t < 20$ | $20 \leqslant t < 40$ | $40 \leqslant t < 60$ | $60 \leqslant t < 80$ |
|---|---|---|---|---|
| Frequency | 55 | 25 | 15 | 5 |

(a) Draw a cumulative frequency graph.
(b) Use your graph to find:
   (i) the median,
   (ii) the interquartile range.

(a) | Make a cumulative frequency table
that can be used to draw the graph.

| Time (mins) less than | 0 | 20 | 40 | 60 | 80 |
|---|---|---|---|---|---|
| Cumulative frequency | 0 | 55 | 80 | 95 | 100 |

(b) Reading from the graph:
   (i) Median = 18 minutes
   (ii) Lower quartile (LQ) = 8 minutes
      Upper quartile (UQ) = 35 minutes
      Interquartile range = UQ − LQ = 35 − 8 = 27 minutes

- A **box plot** is used to represent the range, the median and the quartiles of a distribution.

Mass (kg)

- The box plot shows how the data is spread out and how the middle 50% of data is clustered.

- Box plots can be used to compare two (or more) distributions.

- You should be able to draw and interpret box plots.

**Eg 2** 15 pupils were asked to estimate the size of an angle.
Their estimates, in degrees, are shown.

40   20   38   30   32   45   35   36   40   35   30   40   45   42   25

Draw a box plot to illustrate the data.

> Put the data in order and locate the median, lower quartile and upper quartile.
> Then use these values to draw the box plot.

Size of angle (degrees)

## Exercise 39

1. As part of a lifesaving course a group of students were asked to swim as far as possible wearing shoes and clothes.
The cumulative frequency graph shows the distances swum.

(a) Use the graph to find:
  (i) the median distance,    (ii) the interquartile range.
(b) Draw a box plot to illustrate the distances swum.

**2** A group of children were asked to estimate the weight of a bucket of water.
Their estimates, in kilograms, are shown.

| 10 | 9 | 17.5 | 8 | 7.5 | 5 | 10 | 15 | 12.5 | 20 | 8 | 10 | 14 | 18 | 11 |

(a) Find:
  (i)  the median estimate,
  (ii) the interquartile range of these estimates.
(b) Draw a box plot to represent these estimates.

**3** The cumulative frequency graphs show information about the prices paid for computers and televisions.

(a) Find the median price paid for a television.
(b) Find the interquartile range of the prices paid for computers.
(c) Compare and comment on the prices paid for computers and televisions.

**4** The box plots illustrate the distribution of weights for a sample of eating apples and a sample of cooking apples.

(a) What is the range in the weights of the eating apples?
(b) Which type of apple has the higher median weight?
(c) What is the interquartile range for cooking apples?
(d) Compare and comment on these distributions.

**5** Fred carries out a survey of the times, in seconds, between one car and the next car on a road.
His results are shown in the table.

| Time ($s$ seconds) | $0 \leqslant s < 10$ | $10 \leqslant s < 20$ | $20 \leqslant s < 30$ | $30 \leqslant s < 40$ |
|---|---|---|---|---|
| Frequency | 11 | 31 | 21 | 7 |

(a) How many cars were in the survey?
(b) Draw a cumulative frequency graph to show Fred's results.
(c) Use your graph to estimate the median time.
(d) Use your graph to estimate the percentage of times that were greater than 25 seconds.

Edexcel

## What you need to know

- **Probability** describes how likely or unlikely it is that an event will occur. Probabilities are written as **fractions**, **decimals** or **percentages**.

- How to work out probabilities using **equally likely outcomes**.

$$\text{The probability of an event} = \frac{\text{Number of outcomes in the event}}{\text{Total number of possible outcomes}}$$

**Eg 1** A box contains 7 red pens and 4 blue pens. A pen is taken from the box at random. What is the probability that the pen is blue?

$$P(\text{blue}) = \frac{\text{Number of blue pens}}{\text{Total number of pens}} = \frac{4}{11}$$

> P(blue) stands for the probability that the pen is blue.

- How to estimate probabilities using **relative frequency**.

$$\text{Relative frequency} = \frac{\text{Number of times the event happens in an experiment (or in a survey)}}{\text{Total number of trials in the experiment (or observations in the survey)}}$$

**Eg 2** A spinner is spun 20 times. The results are shown.

| 4 | 1 | 3 | 1 | 4 | 2 | 2 | 4 | 3 | 3 |
| 4 | 1 | 4 | 4 | 3 | 2 | 2 | 1 | 3 | 2 |

What is the relative frequency of getting a 4?

$$\text{Relative frequency} = \frac{\text{Number of 4's}}{\text{Number of spins}} = \frac{6}{20} = 0.3$$

> Relative frequency gives a better estimate of probability the larger the number of trials.

- How to use probabilities to **estimate** the number of times an event occurs in an **experiment** or **observation**.

$$\text{Estimate} = \text{total number of trials (or observations)} \times \text{probability of event}$$

**Eg 3** 1000 raffle tickets are sold. Alan buys some tickets.
The probability that Alan wins first prize is $\frac{1}{50}$.
How many tickets did Alan buy?   Number of tickets $= 1000 \times \frac{1}{50} = 20$

- **Mutually exclusive events** cannot occur at the same time.

$$\text{When A and B are mutually exclusive events:   } P(A \text{ or } B) = P(A) + P(B)$$

**Eg 4** A box contains red, green, blue and yellow counters.
The table shows the probability of getting each colour.

| Colour | Red | Green | Blue | Yellow |
|---|---|---|---|---|
| Probability | 0.4 | 0.25 | 0.25 | 0.1 |

A counter is taken from the box at random.
What is the probability of getting a red or blue counter?

$P(\text{Red or Blue}) = P(\text{Red}) + P(\text{Blue}) = 0.4 + 0.25 = 0.65$

- 
$$\text{The probability of an event, A, \textbf{not happening} is:   } P(\text{not } A) = 1 - P(A)$$

For example, the probability I will get a phone call today is 0.9.
So, the probability I will **not** get a phone call today is $1 - 0.9 = 0.1$.

● How to find all the possible outcomes when two events are combined.
　　By **listing** the outcomes systematically.
　　By using a **possibility space diagram**.
　　By using a **tree diagram**.

● The outcomes of **independent events** do not influence each other.

> When A and B are independent events:   P(A and B) = P(A) × P(B)

**Eg 5**　Box A contains 3 white cubes (W) and 1 blue cube (B).
　　Box B contains 2 white cubes (W) and 3 blue cubes (B).
　　A cube is drawn from each box at random.
　　(a)　Draw a tree diagram to show all the possible outcomes.
　　(b)　Calculate the probability of getting two white cubes.

(a)　**Box A**　　　　**Box B**　　　**Outcome**　　　(b)

| | Box A | Box B | Outcome |
|---|---|---|---|
| | $\frac{3}{4}$ W | $\frac{2}{5}$ W | WW |
| | | $\frac{3}{5}$ B | WB |
| | $\frac{1}{4}$ B | $\frac{2}{5}$ W | BW |
| | | $\frac{3}{5}$ B | BB |

> To calculate P(WW), multiply the probabilities along the branches of the tree diagram.

$$P(WW) = \frac{3}{4} \times \frac{2}{5}$$
$$= \frac{6}{20}$$
$$= \frac{3}{10}$$

● **Conditional probabilities** arise when the probabilities of particular events occurring are affected by other events.

**Eg 6**　In a drawer there are 4 black socks and 2 green socks. Two socks are taken at random. What is the probability that they are both the same colour?

> The probabilities for the second sock are **dependent** on the colour of the first sock.

**1st sock**　　**2nd sock**

| 1st sock | 2nd sock |
|---|---|
| $\frac{4}{6}$ B | $\frac{3}{5}$ B |
| | $\frac{2}{5}$ G |
| $\frac{2}{6}$ G | $\frac{4}{5}$ B |
| | $\frac{1}{5}$ G |

P(same colour) = P(BB) + P(GG)
$$= \left(\frac{4}{6} \times \frac{3}{5}\right) + \left(\frac{2}{6} \times \frac{1}{5}\right)$$
$$= \frac{12}{30} + \frac{2}{30}$$
$$= \frac{14}{30} = \frac{7}{15}$$
P(same colour) $= \frac{7}{15}$

## Exercise 40

**1**　The letters of the word　A　B　B　E　Y　are written on separate cards and placed in a box. A card is taken from the box at random.
　(a)　What is the probability that it is the letter B?
　(b)　The probability that it is a vowel is 0.4.
　　　What is the probability that it is not a vowel?

**2**　Petra has 5 numbered cards. She uses the cards to do this experiment:

> Shuffle the cards and then record the number on the top card.

She repeats the experiment 20 times and gets these results.

　　　　3　　3　　2　　3　　4　　3　　5　　2　　3　　4
　　　　3　　5　　3　　3　　4　　2　　5　　3　　4　　2

　(a)　What is the relative frequency of getting a 3?
　(b)　What numbers do you think are on the five cards? Give a reason for your answer.
　(c)　She repeats the experiment 500 times.
　　　Estimate the number of times she will get a 5. Give a reason for your answer.

**3** Jeff tosses a coin three times.
  (a)  List all the possible outcomes.
  (b)  What is the probability that he gets one head and two tails?

**4** Jack has two fair dice.
One of the dice has 6 faces numbered from 1 to 6.
The other dice has 4 faces numbered from 1 to 4.

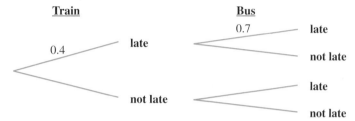

Jack is going to throw the two dice.
He will add the scores on the two dice to get the total.
Work out the probability that he will get
  (a)  a total of 7,
  (b)  a total of less than 5.         Edexcel

**5** On Tuesday Jim has to catch a bus and a train to get to work.
The probability that the train is late is 0.4.
The probability that the bus is late is 0.7.
  (a)  Copy and complete the tree diagram.

**Train**                    **Bus**

                            0.7        late

                  late

   0.4                              not late

                                late

                not late

                                not late

  (b)  What is the probability that both the bus and the train are late?
  (c)  What is the probability that either the train or the bus is late but not both?

**6** Peter and Asif are both taking their driving test for a motor cycle for the first time.
The table below gives the probabilities that they will pass the test at the first attempt.

|  | Probability of passing at first attempt |
|---|---|
| Peter | 0.6 |
| Asif | 0.7 |

On a particular day 1000 people will take the test for the first time.
For each person the probability that they will pass the test at the first attempt is the same as
the probability that Asif will pass the test at the first attempt.
  (a)  Work out an estimate for how many of these 1000 people are likely to pass the test at the
      first attempt.
  (b)  Calculate the probability that both Peter and Asif will pass the test at the first attempt.
  (c)  Calculate the probability that Peter will pass the test at the first attempt and Asif will fail
      the test at the first attempt.         Edexcel

**7** The probability that a team will win a game is always 0.8
The team plays $n$ games.
The probability that the team will win every game is less than $\frac{1}{4}$.
Calculate the smallest possible value of $n$.         Edexcel

**8**   (a)  Bag $X$ contains 3 red counters, 6 blue counters and 3 green counters.
      Bag $Y$ contains 4 red counters and 2 blue counters.
      A bag is chosen at random and a counter is then taken from the bag.
      (i)  Draw a tree diagram to show all the possible outcomes.
      (ii)  What is the probability of getting a red counter?
  (b)  Bag $Z$ contains 5 red counters and 2 green counters.
      Two counters are taken from bag $Z$ at random.
      What is the probability of getting two counters of the same colour?

# Handling Data
# Non-calculator Paper

Do not use a calculator for this exercise.

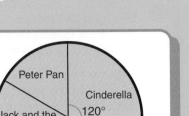

**1** Sylvester did a survey to find the most popular pantomime.
The results of his survey are shown in the pie chart.

(a) 20 people chose Aladdin.
How many people were included in the survey?

(b) Sylvester said, "30% of people chose Cinderella."
Is he correct?
Explain your answer.

**2** A box contains 20 plastic ducks.
3 of the ducks are green, 10 are blue and the rest are yellow.
A duck is taken from the box at random.
What is the probability that it is   (a)   green,        (b)   yellow?

**3** Bhavana asked some people which region their favourite football team came from.
The table shows her results.

| Region | Midlands | London | Southern England | Northern England |
|---|---|---|---|---|
| Frequency | 22 | 36 | 8 | 24 |

Complete an accurate pie chart to show these results.                              Edexcel

**4** The lengths of 20 bolts, in centimetres, is shown.

    7.4    5.8    4.5    5.0    6.5    6.6    7.0    5.4    4.8    6.4
    5.4    6.2    7.2    5.5    4.8    6.5    5.0    6.0    6.5    6.8

(a) Draw a stem and leaf diagram to show this information.
(b) What is the range in the lengths of these bolts?

**5** The table shows information about a group of students.

|  | Can speak French | Cannot speak French |
|---|---|---|
| Male | 5 | 20 |
| Female | 12 | 38 |

(a) One of these students is chosen at random.
What is the probability that the student can speak French?

(b) Pru says,

>*"If a female student is chosen at random she is more likely to be able to speak French than if a male student is chosen at random."*

Is she correct?
Explain your answer.

**6** Some people were asked how many National Lottery tickets they bought last week.
The results are shown in the table.

| Number of tickets | 0 | 1 | 2 | 3 | 4 | 5 | 6 |
|---|---|---|---|---|---|---|---|
| Number of people | 2 | 7 | 5 | 2 | 0 | 3 | 1 |

(a) Which number of tickets is the mode?
(b) Work out the median number of tickets.
(c) Find the mean number of tickcts.                              Edexcel

**7** Linzi is doing a survey to find if there should be a supermarket in her neighbourhood. This is one of her questions.

> "Do you agree that having a supermarket in the neighbourhood would make it easier for you to do your shopping and if we did have one would you use it?"

Give two reasons why this question is unsuitable in its present form.

**8** Mrs Wild drives to school each morning.
The probability that she parks her car at the front of the school is 0.6.
The probability that she parks her car at the side of the school is 0.3.
(a)  What is the probability that she will park either at the front **or** at the side of the school tomorrow morning?
(b)  In the next 200 school mornings, approximately how many times will Mrs Wild **not** park either at the front or at the side of the school?

Edexcel

**9** The graph shows the distribution of the best height jumped by each girl in a high jump competition.

(a)  Which class interval contains the median height?
(b)  Calculate an estimate of the mean of these heights.

**10** A factory makes boxes of cereal.
A box of cereal can be either underweight or the correct weight or overweight.
The probability that a box of cereal selected at random is underweight is 1%.
The probability that a box of cereal selected at random is overweight is 3%.
(a)  Work out the probability that a box selected at random will be the correct weight.

All the underweight boxes of cereal are removed.
All boxes that are the correct weight or overweight are put in an empty warehouse.
A box of cereal is then selected at random from the warehouse.
(b)  Work out the probability that a box of cereal selected at random from the warehouse will be overweight.
Give your answer as a fraction in its simplest form.

Edexcel

**11** At a fete Jessie has one go on the hoopla and one go on the darts.
The probability she wins a prize on the hoopla is 0.3.
The probability she wins a prize on the darts is 0.4.
(a)  Copy and complete the tree diagram for these two events.

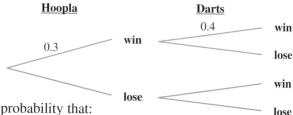

(b)  Calculate the probability that:
   (i)   she does not win a prize,
   (ii)  she wins only one prize.

**12** Students in Year 11 were asked to write an essay on "Popstars".

(a) The table shows the distribution of the times taken by male students to complete the essay.

| Time (t minutes) | $10 \leqslant t < 20$ | $20 \leqslant t < 30$ | $30 \leqslant t < 40$ | $40 \leqslant t < 50$ |
|---|---|---|---|---|
| Frequency | 8 | 27 | 19 | 6 |

(i) Draw a cumulative frequency graph for the data.
(ii) Use your graph to estimate the median and the interquartile range.

(b) The box plot illustrates the distribution of the times taken by female students to complete the essay.

Time (minutes)

Estimate the median and the interquartile range.

(c) Compare and comment on the times taken by male students and the times taken by female students to complete the essay.

**13** The table shows some information about the members of a golf club.

| Age range | Male | Female | Total |
|---|---|---|---|
| Under 18 | 29 | 10 | 39 |
| 18 to 30 | 82 | 21 | 103 |
| 31 to 50 | 147 | 45 | 192 |
| Over 50 | 91 | 29 | 120 |
| Total number of members | | | 454 |

The club secretary carries out a survey of the members.
He chooses a sample, stratified both by age and by gender, of 90 of the 454 members.
Work out an estimate of the number of male members, in the age range 31 to 50, he would have to sample.

Edexcel

**14** A survey was carried out to find the average length of a garden.
The histogram shows the results.

(a) How many gardens were included in the survey?
(b) Use the histogram to estimate:
   (i) the percentage of gardens less than 12 metres in length,
   (ii) the median length of a garden.

**15** In a class of 25 students, 5 are left-handed and the rest are right-handed.
Two students are chosen at random, one at a time.
Calculate the probability that:
(a) they are both left-handed,
(b) one is left-handed and one is right-handed.

You may use a calculator for this exercise.

**1** The stem and leaf diagram shows the ages of people taking part in a survey.

| male | | | female | 1\|5 means 15 years old |

```
              male                        female         1│5 means 15 years old
                              0 │ 9
 6  6  6  6  5  5  5  5  5  5  1 │ 5  5  5  6  6  6
                              2 │ 4  5  8  9
                              3 │ 1  3  5
                              4 │ 9
```

Give three reasons why the results of this survey may be biased.

**2** Karina is playing a game with these cards.   **X**   **Y**   **1**   **1**   **3**

One card is taken at random from the letters.
One card is taken at random from the numbers.
(a)  List all the possible outcomes.
(b)  Explain why the probability of getting   **X**   **1**   is not $\frac{1}{4}$.

**3** Corrin throws a dice 40 times. Her results are shown.

| Score | 1 | 2 | 3 | 4 | 5 | 6 |
|---|---|---|---|---|---|---|
| Frequency | 7 | 6 | 7 | 6 | 6 | 8 |

(a)  Which score is the mode?
(b)  Calculate the mean score.
(c)  What is the median score?

**4** Ten men took part in a long jump competition.
The table shows the heights of the ten men and the best jumps they made.

| Best jump (m) | 5.33 | 6.00 | 5.00 | 5.95 | 4.80 | 5.72 | 4.60 | 5.80 | 4.40 | 5.04 |
|---|---|---|---|---|---|---|---|---|---|---|
| Height of men (m) | 1.70 | 1.80 | 1.65 | 1.75 | 1.65 | 1.74 | 1.60 | 1.75 | 1.60 | 1.67 |

(a)  Plot the points as a scatter graph.
(b)  Describe the relationship between the heights of the men and the best jumps they made.
(c)  Draw a line of best fit.
(d)  Use your line of best fit to estimate
   (i)   the height of a man who could make a best jump of 5.2 m,
   (ii)  the best jump of a man of height 1.73 m.
   *Edexcel*

**5** A youth club has 60 members.
40 of the members are boys.
20 of the members are girls.
The mean number of videos watched last week by all 60 members was 2.8.
The mean number of videos watched last week by the 40 boys was 3.3.
Calculate the mean number of videos watched last week by the 20 girls.   *Edexcel*

**6** Grace and Gemma were carrying out a survey on the food people eat in the school canteen.
Grace wrote the question:   *"Which foods do you eat?"*
Gemma said that this question was too vague.
Write down two ways in which this question could be improved.   *Edexcel*

**7** Jason grows potatoes. He weighed 100 potatoes and recorded the weights to the nearest gram. The table shows information about the weights ($w$) of the 100 potatoes.

| Weight ($w$ grams) | Frequency |
|---|---|
| $0 \leqslant w < 20$ | 0 |
| $20 \leqslant w < 40$ | 18 |
| $40 \leqslant w < 60$ | 28 |
| $60 \leqslant w < 80$ | 25 |
| $80 \leqslant w < 100$ | 19 |
| $100 \leqslant w < 120$ | 10 |

(a) Draw a frequency polygon to show this information.
(b) Work out an estimate for the mean weight of these potatoes.
(c) Find the class interval that contains the median.     Edexcel

**8** Tony throws a biased dice 100 times. The table shows his results.

| Score | 1 | 2 | 3 | 4 | 5 | 6 |
|---|---|---|---|---|---|---|
| Frequency | 12 | 13 | 17 | 10 | 18 | 30 |

He throws the dice once more.
(a) Find an estimate for the probability that he will get a 6.

Emma has a biased coin. The probability that the biased coin will land on a head is 0.7.
Emma is going to throw the coin 250 times.
(b) Work out an estimate for the number of times the coin will land on a head.     Edexcel

**9** The table gives information about the ages, in years, of 100 aeroplanes.

| Age ($t$ years) | $0 < t \leqslant 5$ | $5 < t \leqslant 10$ | $10 < t \leqslant 15$ | $15 < t \leqslant 20$ | $20 < t \leqslant 25$ |
|---|---|---|---|---|---|
| Frequency | 41 | 26 | 20 | 10 | 3 |

(a) Work out an estimate of the mean age of the aeroplanes.
(b) Copy and complete the cumulative frequency table.

| Age ($t$ years) | Cumulative frequency |
|---|---|
| $0 < t \leqslant 5$ | |
| $0 < t \leqslant 10$ | |

(c) Draw a cumulative frequency graph for your table.
(d) Use your graph to find an estimate of the upper quartile of the ages.     Edexcel

**10** Sharon has 12 computer discs. Five of the discs are red. Seven of the discs are black.
She keeps all the discs in a box. Sharon removes one disc at random.
She records its colour and replaces it in the box.
Sharon removes a second disc at random, and again records its colour.
(a) Copy and complete the tree diagram.

(b) Calculate the probability that the two discs removed:
    (i) will both be red,      (ii) will be different colours.     Edexcel

**11** Here is a list of the last 8 quarterly gas bills for a householder.

| Month | Jan. | Apr. | Jul. | Oct. | Jan. | Apr. | Jul. | Oct. |
|---|---|---|---|---|---|---|---|---|
| Amount | £67 | £188 | £27 | £18 | £139 | £103 | £23 | £27 |

Calculate the first two 4-point moving averages for this data.

**12** Giles has two chickens.
The probability that a chicken will lay an egg on any day is 0.7.
(a) What is the probability that both chickens will lay an egg on Sunday?
(b) What is the probability that only one chicken will lay an egg on Monday?

**13** Ruben is doing a survey of the use of mobile phones among students at his school.
(a) Give reasons why a sample of the sixth form only, may be biased.
(b) Ruben decides to take a stratified random sample of 10% of all the students in the school.
    (i) Describe how he chooses his sample.
    (ii) Give one advantage this method has over a simple random sample.

**14** The table shows the distribution of the times, in minutes, that people had to wait for their meals at a restaurant.

| Time ($t$ minutes) | $0 \leqslant t < 10$ | $10 \leqslant t < 15$ | $15 \leqslant t < 25$ | $25 \leqslant t < 40$ |
|---|---|---|---|---|
| Frequency | 25 | 21 | 24 | 9 |

(a) Draw a histogram to represent these waiting times.
(b) Estimate the median waiting time.
(c) Estimate how many people had to wait more than 30 minutes for their meal.

**15** The diagram shows six counters.
Each counter has a number on it.

Anil puts the six counters in a bag.
He chooses two counters at random **without** replacement.
(a) Calculate the probability that **both** counters will have the number 2 on them.
(b) Calculate the probability that the **sum** of the numbers on the two counters will be 4.

*Edexcel*

**16** The teachers at Redmount School want to find out what the pupils think about school uniform.
Altogether there are 360 pupils in Year 7 and Year 8.
There are 244 pupils in Year 7.
There are 116 pupils in Year 8.
The teachers survey a representative sample of 40 of the pupils.
How many pupils should be chosen from each Year group?

*Edexcel*

**17** In a bag there are 10 counters.
4 of the counters are red and 6 of the counters are blue.
Ann and Betty are going to play a game.
Ann is going to remove 2 counters at random from the bag.
She will not put them back.
If both counters are the same colour, Ann will win the game.
(a) Calculate the probability that Ann will win the game.

If the counters are different colours, it will be Betty's turn.
Betty will remove **one** counter at random from the 8 counters still in the bag.
If the counter is red, Betty will win the game.
If the counter is blue, the result will be a draw.
(b) Calculate the probability that the result will be a draw.

*Edexcel*

# Non-calculator Paper

Do not use a calculator for this exercise.

**1** **$32 \times 129 = 4128$**

Write down the value of   (a)   $3.2 \times 1.29$,        (b)   $0.32 \times 129\,000$.        Edexcel

**2** $A$ is the point $(-4, -1)$.   $B$ is the point $(2, 3)$.
What is the midpoint of the line segment $AB$?

**3** Shreena has a bag of 20 sweets.
10 of the sweets are red. 3 of the sweets are black. The rest of the sweets are white.
Shreena chooses one sweet at random.
What is the probability that Shreena will choose   (a)   a red sweet,      (b)   a white sweet?
Edexcel

**4** (a)   Write $\frac{7}{9}$ as a decimal. Give your answer correct to two decimal places.

(b)   Write $33\%$,   $0.3$,   $\frac{8}{25}$   and   $\frac{1}{3}$   in order of size, smallest first.

**5** To calculate the number of mince pies, $m$, to make for a Christmas Party for $p$ people,
Donna uses the formula   $m = 2p + 10$.
(a)   How many mince pies would she make for a party of 12 people?
(b)   Donna makes 60 mince pies for another party.
      How many people are expected at this party?

**6** In the diagram $PQ$ and $RS$ are straight lines.

Work out the values of $a$, $b$ and $c$.
Give a reason for each of your answers.

Edexcel

**7** The numbers on these cards are coded.
The sum of the numbers on these 3 cards is 41.

| $x$ | $2x - 1$ | $3x$ |
|---|---|---|

(a)   Form an equation in $x$.
(b)   By solving your equation, find the numbers on the cards.

**8** A quiz has 40 questions.
(a)   Lenny gets 34 questions right. What percentage of the questions did he get right?
(b)   12 boys took part in the quiz. The ratio of boys to girls taking part in the quiz is $3 : 5$.
      How many girls took part?

**9** Solve the equations.   (a)   $11x + 5 = x + 25$        (b)   $3(4y - 9) = 81$        Edexcel

**10** (a)   Write as a product of its prime factors:   (i)   48,        (ii)   108.
(b)   Hence, find the least common multiple of 48 and 108.

**11** (a)   Draw and label the lines   $y = x + 1$   and   $x + y = 3$   for values of $x$ from $-1$ to 3.
(b)   Write down the coordinates of the point where the lines cross.

**12** A farmer has a crop circle in his field. The circle has a circumference of $12\pi$ metres.
Calculate, in terms of $\pi$, the area of the circle.

**13** A concrete block weighs 11 kg, correct to the nearest kilogram.
Write down the greatest and least possible weight of the block.

14. A sequence begins: 2, 5, 8, 11, ...
    Write in terms of $n$, the $n$th term of the sequence.

15. The diagram shows the positions of shapes $P$, $Q$ and $R$.

    (a) Describe fully the single transformation which takes:
        (i) $P$ onto $Q$,    (ii) $P$ onto $R$.

    (b) Copy shape $Q$ onto squared paper and draw an enlargement of the shape with scale factor $-2$, centre $(0, 3)$.

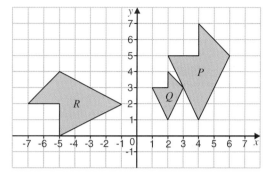

16. The table shows information about the number of fillings the students in a class had last year.

| Number of students | 0 | 1 | 2 | 3 | More than 3 |
|---|---|---|---|---|---|
| Number of fillings | 10 | 5 | 4 | 2 | 1 |

    The headteacher is to choose a student at random from the class.
    Find the probability that she will choose a student who had
    (a) exactly 1 filling,    (b) 2 or more fillings,    (c) either 1 filling or 2 fillings.    Edexcel

17. (a) Copy and complete the table of values for $y = x^2 - 3x + 1$.

| $x$ | $-1$ | 0 | 1 | 2 | 3 | 4 |
|---|---|---|---|---|---|---|
| $y$ | | 1 | $-1$ | | | 5 |

    (b) Draw the graph of $y = x^2 - 3x + 1$ for values of $x$ from $-1$ to 4.
    (c) Use your graph to solve the equation $x^2 - 3x + 1 = 0$.

18. Cocoa is sold in cylindrical tins. The height of a tin is 7.9 cm. The radius of a tin is 4.1 cm.
    Use approximations to estimate the volume of a tin. Show all your working.

19. (a) Solve   (i) $7 - \dfrac{3x}{2} = 11$,    (ii) $\dfrac{4}{y} + 7 = 2$.

    (b) (i) Factorise $x^2 + 4x - 12$.
        (ii) Hence, or otherwise, solve $x^2 + 4x - 12 = 0$.    Edexcel

20. Solve the simultaneous equations   $4x + y = 4$   and   $2x + 3y = -3$.    Edexcel

21. Work out.   (a) $2\frac{1}{2} - 1\frac{2}{3}$    (b) $2\frac{1}{2} \div 1\frac{2}{3}$

22. The diameter of an atom is 0.000 000 03 m.
    (a) Write 0.000 000 03 in standard form.

    Using the most powerful microscope, the smallest objects which can be seen have diameters which are **one hundredth** of the diameter of an atom.
    (b) Calculate the diameter, in metres, of the smallest object which can be seen using this microscope. Give your answer in standard form.    Edexcel

23. Hugh buys a box of fireworks. After lighting 40% of the fireworks he has 24 fireworks left.
    How many fireworks did he buy?

24. You are given the formula $a = bc^2$.
    (a) Calculate the value of $a$ when $b = 100$ and $c = -\frac{3}{5}$.
    (b) Rearrange the formula to give $c$ in terms of $a$ and $b$.

25. (a) Expand and simplify $(2x + 1)(x - 3)$.
    (b) Simplify $3a^3 \times 2ab^2$.
    (c) Factorise completely   (i) $2t^2 + 4t$,    (ii) $9x^2 - 4$.    Edexcel

**26** On a diagram, shade the region which satisfies these inequalities:
$$1 \leqslant y \leqslant 3, \qquad 2y \geqslant x \qquad \text{and} \qquad 2x \geqslant y + 1.$$

**27** (a) Simplify $x^4 \div x^{-3}$

(b) Find the value of $x$ for which $4^{\frac{x}{2}} = 32$. *Edexcel*

**28** The sketches show the graphs of four equations. Write down the equation for each graph.

(a)
(b)
(c)
(d)

**29** $A$, $B$, $C$ and $D$ are points on the circumference of the circle, centre $O$.
Angle $ACD = 72°$. $ABD$ is an isosceles triangle with $BA = BD$.
(a) Calculate the size of angle $ADB$.

$AOC$ is a diameter.
(b) Calculate the size of angle $BAC$.

Tangents are drawn to the circle at $A$ and $B$.
These tangents meet at $P$.
(c) Calculate the size of the angle $APB$. *Edexcel*

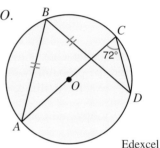

**30** (a) Evaluate (i) $16^{\frac{3}{4}}$, (ii) $27^{-\frac{2}{3}}$.

(b) Show that $\dfrac{2}{\sqrt{3}} - \dfrac{\sqrt{3}}{2} = \dfrac{\sqrt{3}}{6}$.

**31** **Prove** that when 2 is subtracted from the sum of the squares of three consecutive integers, the answer is always 3 times a square number. *Edexcel*

**32** $OAXB$ is a parallelogram. $\overrightarrow{OA} = \mathbf{a}$ and $\overrightarrow{OB} = \mathbf{b}$.

$M$ is a point on $OA$ such that $\overrightarrow{OM} = \frac{1}{3}\mathbf{a}$.

$N$ is a point on $OB$ such that $\overrightarrow{ON} = \frac{2}{3}\mathbf{b}$.

Find, in terms of $\mathbf{a}$ and $\mathbf{b}$, $\overrightarrow{AB}$, $\overrightarrow{OX}$ and $\overrightarrow{MN}$.

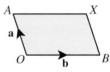

**33** (a) Simplify. $\dfrac{4x^2 - 6x}{2x^2 + 3x - 9}$

(b) Rearrange the formula $p = \dfrac{mn}{m + n}$ to give $m$ in terms of $p$ and $n$.

(c) Solve the simultaneous equations $x + 2y = 5$ and $x = \dfrac{2}{y}$.

**34** A sketch of $y = f(x)$ for $0° \leqslant x \leqslant 360°$ is shown.
Draw sketches to show each of these
transformations of $y = f(x)$.
(a) $y = f(x) + 2$
(b) $y = 2f(x)$
(c) $y = f(2x)$

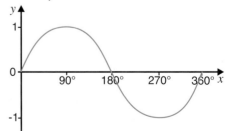

**35** There are 25 beads in a bag.
Some of the beads are red. All the other beads are blue.
Kate picks two beads at random without replacement.
The probability that she will pick 2 red beads is 0.07.
Calculate the probability that the two beads she picks will be of different colours. *Edexcel*

# Calculator Paper ●●●●●●●●●●●●●●●●

You may use a calculator for this exercise.

**1**  (a)  Simplify.  (i)  $4x + 7y + 2x - 3y$        (ii)  $2pq + pq$

(b)  Factorise.  $3t - 12$                                           Edexcel

**2**  Bob cycles from home to work. The travel graph shows his journey.

(a)  On his way to work Bob stopped to buy a newspaper.
     At what time did he stop?
(b)  (i)  During which part of his journey did Bob cycle fastest?
          Give a reason for your answer.
     (ii)  Calculate his average speed in kilometres per hour for this part of his journey.

**3**  The table shows the birth rate and the life expectancy for 12 countries.

| Birth rate | 13 | 17 | 21 | 25 | 28 | 30 | 31 | 34 | 38 | 41 | 44 | 47 |
|---|---|---|---|---|---|---|---|---|---|---|---|---|
| Life expectancy (years) | 75 | 73 | 71 | 68 | 65 | 62 | 61 | 65 | 61 | 56 | 51 | 49 |

(a)  Plot the information as a scatter graph.
(b)  Describe the relationship between the birth rate and the life expectancy.
(c)  Draw a line of best fit on your scatter graph.

The birth rate in a country is 42.
(d)  Use your scatter graph to estimate the life expectancy in that country.          Edexcel

**4**  The perimeter of the pentagon is 200 cm.
Work out the value of $x$.

Edexcel

**5**  A hang glider flies 2.8 km on a bearing of 070° from $P$ to $Q$ and then 2 km on a bearing of 200° from $Q$ to $R$.
(a)  Make a scale drawing to show the flight of the hang glider from $P$ to $Q$ to $R$.
     Use a scale of 1 cm to 200 m.
(b)  From $R$ the hang glider flies directly back to $P$.
     Use your drawing to find the distance and bearing of $P$ from $R$.

**6**  Solve the equations.
(a)  $3y + 7 = 28$        (b)  $2(3p + 2) = 19$        (c)  $3t - 4 = 5t - 10$          Edexcel

**7** The diagram shows a prism. The cross-section of the prism is a trapezium.
(a) Work out the volume of the prism.

The prism is made out of gold.
Gold has a density of 19.3 grams per cm³.
(b) Work out the mass of the prism.
Give your answer in kilograms.

Edexcel

**8** A solution of the equation $x^3 - 9x = 5$ is between 3 and 4.
Use the method of trial and improvement to find this solution.
Give your answer correct to 2 decimal places. You must show **all** your working. Edexcel

**9** Marcus collected some pebbles. He weighed each pebble.
The grouped frequency table gives some information about weights.

| Weight ($w$ grams) | $50 \leqslant w < 60$ | $60 \leqslant w < 70$ | $70 \leqslant w < 80$ | $80 \leqslant w < 90$ | $90 \leqslant w < 100$ |
|---|---|---|---|---|---|
| Frequency | 5 | 9 | 22 | 27 | 17 |

Work out an estimate for the mean weight of the pebbles. Edexcel

**10** Bill gave his three daughters a total of £32.40.
The money was shared in the ratios 4 : 3 : 2.
Jane had the largest share.
Work out how much money Bill gave to Jane.

Edexcel

**11**

The diagram shows a semi-circle with diameter $AB$.
$C$ is a point on the circumference.
$\angle ACB = 90°$. $AC = 6$ cm and $CB = 8$ cm.
Calculate the area of the shaded triangle as a percentage of the area of the semi-circle.

**12** (a) Solve the inequality $4x - 3 > 2$.
(b) Write down the smallest whole number that is a solution of the inequality $4x - 3 > 2$.
Edexcel

**13** The diagram shows the positions of three schools, $P$, $Q$ and $R$.
School $P$ is 8 kilometres due West of School $Q$.
School $R$ is 3 kilometres due North of School $Q$.
(a) Calculate the size of the angle marked $x°$.
Give your answer correct to one decimal place.

Simon's house is 8 kilometres due East of School $Q$.
(b) Calculate the bearing of Simon's house from school $R$.

Edexcel

**14** (a) The frequency distribution table gives information about the distances travelled to school by pupils at a primary school.

| Distance ($k$ kilometres) | $0 \leqslant k < 1$ | $1 \leqslant k < 2$ | $2 \leqslant k < 3$ | $3 \leqslant k < 4$ | $4 \leqslant k < 5$ |
|---|---|---|---|---|---|
| Frequency | 36 | 76 | 28 | 12 | 8 |

(i) Draw a cumulative frequency graph to illustrate the data.
(ii) Use your graph to find the median and the interquartile range.
(b) A survey of the distances travelled to school by pupils at a secondary school gave the following information.

| | | | |
|---|---|---|---|
| Shortest distance | 0.2 km | Median | 2.8 km |
| Longest distance | 9.6 km | Lower quartile | 2.0 km |
| | | Upper quartile | 3.4 km |

Draw a box plot to illustrate the data.
(c) Compare and comment on the distances travelled to school by pupils at these schools.

**15** Calculate the value of $\dfrac{5.98 \times 10^8 + 4.32 \times 10^9}{6.14 \times 10^{-2}}$.

Give your answer in standard form correct to 3 significant figures. *Edexcel*

**16** $y$ is inversely proportional to the square of $x$ and $y = 2.4$ when $x = 2.5$
Find the value of $x$ when $y = 60$.

**17** Speedboats race around the triangular circuit $A \to B \to C \to A$,
as shown in the diagram.
$AB = 5.0\,\text{km}$, $BC = 7.0\,\text{km}$ and angle $BAC = 60°$.
(a) Show that the length of $AC$, $x$ km, satisfies the
equation $x^2 - 5x - 24 = 0$.

The speedboats are taking part in a 100 km race.
(b) By calculating the value of $x$, work out how many times
around the circuit, $ABC$, the speedboats should travel. *Edexcel*

**18**

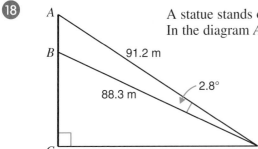

A statue stands on a column.
In the diagram $AB$ represents the statue and $BC$ represents the column.

Angle $ACD = 90°$. Angle $BDA = 2.8°$.
$AD = 91.2\,\text{m}$ and $BD = 88.3\,\text{m}$.
$ABC$ is a vertical straight line.

(a) Calculate the height, $AB$, of the statue.
(b) Calculate the height, $BC$, of the column. *Edexcel*

**19** A cone has a height of 18 cm and the radius of its base is 3 cm.
(a) Calculate the volume of the cone.

The measurements of the cone are correct to the nearest millimetre.
(b) Write down the lower bound of the radius of the cone.
(c) Calculate the difference between the upper and lower bounds
of the volume of the cone expressed as a percentage of the
volume of the cone found in part (a).

*Edexcel*

**20** Express as a single fraction $\dfrac{1}{2x + 3} + \dfrac{1}{2x - 1}$. *Edexcel*

**21** A health club has three categories of membership.
The number of members in each category is shown in the table.

| Type of membership | under 18 | 18 to 64 | 65 and over |
|---|---|---|---|
| Male | 11 | 30 | 7 |
| Female | 13 | 47 | 12 |

A stratified random sample of 20 members is chosen.
(a) What is the ratio of males to females in the sample? Give your answer in the form $1 : n$.
(b) How many members from the "under 18" category will be in the sample?

**22** The diagram shows the curve with equation $y = \text{f}(x)$, where $\text{f}(x) = x^2 - 2x - 3$.
(a) Copy the diagram and sketch the curve with equation $y = \text{f}(x - 2)$.
Label the points where this curve cuts the $x$ axis.

The curve with equation $y = \text{f}(x)$ meets the curve with
equation $y = \text{f}(x - a)$ at the point $P$.
(b) Calculate the $x$ coordinate of the point $P$.
Give your answer in terms of $a$.

The curve with equation $y = x^2 - 2x - 3$ is reflected in the $y$ axis.
(c) Find the equation of this new curve. *Edexcel*

119

# Index